CONTENTS

Krindlekrax
by Philip Ridley

CREDITS

Published by Scholastic Ltd,
Villiers House,
Clarendon Avenue,
Leamington Spa,
Warwickshire CV32 5PR
Text © Huw Thomas
© 1998 Scholastic Ltd
  2 3 4 5 6 7 8 9 0   9 0 1 2 3 4 5 6 7

Author Huw Thomas
Editor Joel Lane
Series designer Lynne Joesbury
Designer Glynis Edwards
Illustrations Mark Robertson
Cover illustration Mark Robertson

Designed using QuarkXpress

British Library Cataloguing-in-Publication Data
A catalogue record for this book is available
from the British Library.

ISBN 0-590-53860-8

ACKNOWLEDGEMENTS

Penguin Books Ltd for the supply of a
photograph of Philip Ridley by Bridget Jones
© Bridget Jones.
Mark Robertson for the newly illustrated front
cover based on the original *Krindlekrax* cover
© 1998, Mark Robertson.
A.P. Watt Limited for the use of extracts from
Meterorite Spoon by Philip Ridley © 1994, Philip
Ridley (1994, Viking) and *Dakota of the White
Flats* by Philip Ridley © 1989, Philip Ridley (1989,
Viking) and especially for the use of extracts,
adaptations and illustrations from *Krindlekrax* by
Philip Ridley Text © 1991, Philip Ridley, Illustrations
© 1991, Mark Robertson (1991, Jonathan Cape).

Every effort has been made to trace copyright
holders and the publishers apologize for any
inadvertent omissions.

INTRODUCTION

Words from the author

Here are some comments from Philip Ridley, the author of *Krindlekrax:*

> The first things
> I read were comics... I see
> their influence in my
> writing.

> What I do
> when I go around schools
> is get children interested
> in language, the power
> of words.

> Why should a
> run-down street be less
> beautiful than a field of
> daisies?

> Children... love the
> pyrotechnics of words.

> Children who read
> my books like the challenge of how
> quickly they're moving through the
> story, how so much happens in such
> a short space of a chapter.

● As you read *Krindlekrax*, pause every so often to re-read this page. Think about how Philip Ridley's comments relate to the story and your understanding of it.

Looking at the cover

● Look at this diagram. It shows some important parts of the cover of *Krindlekrax:*

Blurb

Review quotes

Title

Picture

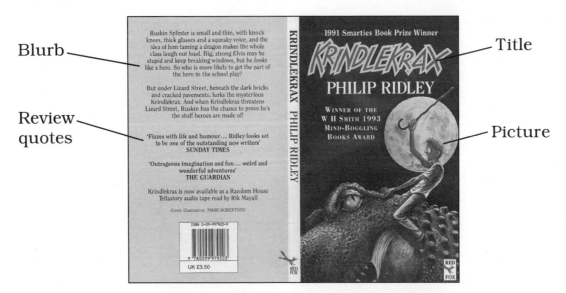

● Look at the cover. What things does it tell you about the book? What questions do you want to ask after reading the cover?

● Fill in the table below:

● In the 'Observations' column, write some things you have learned from looking at the parts of the cover.

● In the 'Questions' column, write some questions you want to ask about the story after looking at the parts of the cover.

	Observations	Questions
Title		
Picture		
Blurb		
Review quote		

What is a hero?

● Read the first line of the story.

● What do you think of when you read the word 'heroine' or 'hero'?

_____

_____

● On the chart below, write the names of three heroines or heroes from different stories. Write down some facts about them.

Story: _____

Heroine/Hero: _____

Notes: _____

_____

Story: _____

Heroine/Hero: _____

Notes: _____

_____

Story: _____

Heroine/Hero: _____

Notes: _____

_____

● Now look at the illustration above the start of chapter 1, and read the opening pages of the story.

● Ruskin thinks he is going to be the hero. Is Ruskin like the heroes and heroines you have written about? Why?

_____

_____

Lizard Street

This is a picture of Lizard Street. As you read *Krindlekrax*, you can look at this picture to see where different parts of the story took place.

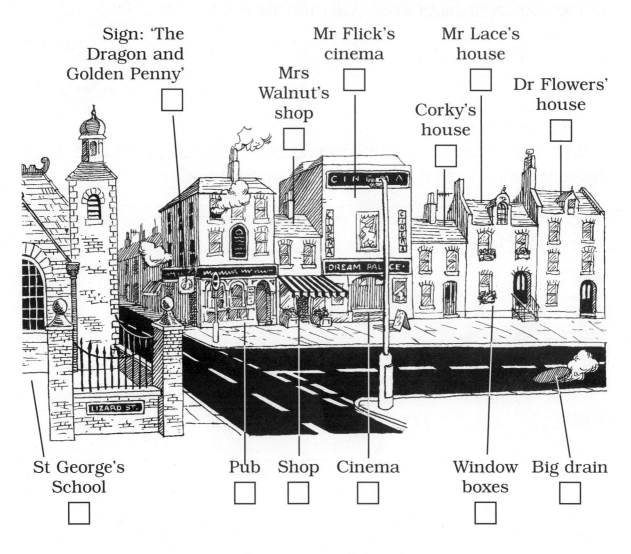

● As you meet each new character, point to the house where he or she lives.

● All of the places and things labelled on this picture are mentioned in the story. As you find them, put a tick in the box for each one.

● Note the pages in the story where these things are first mentioned:

● the pub sign   page ____

● Mr Lace's window boxes   page ____

● the wobbly drain cover   page ____

Meet the Splinters

As readers, we find out about characters in lots of different ways. We look at the things they do or the things they say. The way in which characters are made up in a story is called **characterization**.

● Read Chapter 1. Think: what have you found out about Ruskin Splinter and his parents?

● Draw one of the Splinter family in the box on the left, then fill in the boxes on the right by writing a few notes on that character's appearance and some of the things he or she says and does.

_____ Splinter

What does he or she look like?

What does he or she say?

What does he or she do?

● Try answering these questions for some more characters as you read on.

Building the suspense

● Read up to the end of Chapter 4. Notice how many times Corky is about to explain something about Lizard Street to Ruskin, but is interrupted and doesn't say it.

Suspense in a story is the effect of making the reader wait to find something important out. The reader is 'kept in suspense'.

● Find the three interruptions that stop Corky explaining things to Ruskin in this chapter. Describe them in the boxes on this 'journey home' chart:

the pub

the shop

the cinema

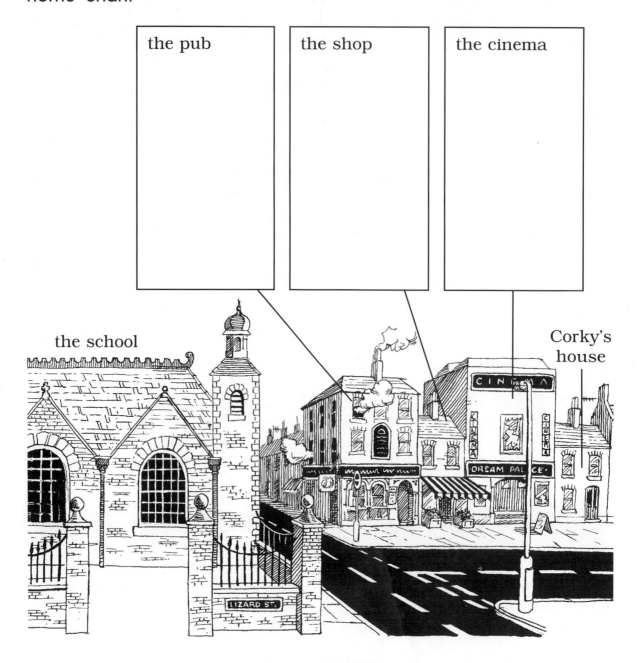

the school

Corky's house

In the sewers

Where does the water go after it goes down the plughole?

Where do the drains take the rainwater to?

Where does the waste go when we flush the toilet?

The answer to these questions is: the **sewers**.

Sewers are large tunnels carrying water and various kinds of waste underneath the city. They can be big enough for people to walk round in.

● Imagine you were in a sewer. Describe what you think it would be like.

> I think

● Now read the first two pages of chapter 5. What does Corky say the sewers are like?

> Corky says

● How do your views compare with Corky's?

What happened that night?

● Read to the end of Chapter 8.
When Winston gets drunk, he tells Ruskin the story of the baby crocodile. This story tells us about something that happened before Ruskin was born.

● Make a list of the other people who were in the pub that night when Winston offered to lend a baby crocodile to Mr Cave.

● Now choose one of the characters in your list and put a circle around his or her name. Imagine you are that character, telling Ruskin about what happened all those years ago. Re-read chapter 8 to help you.

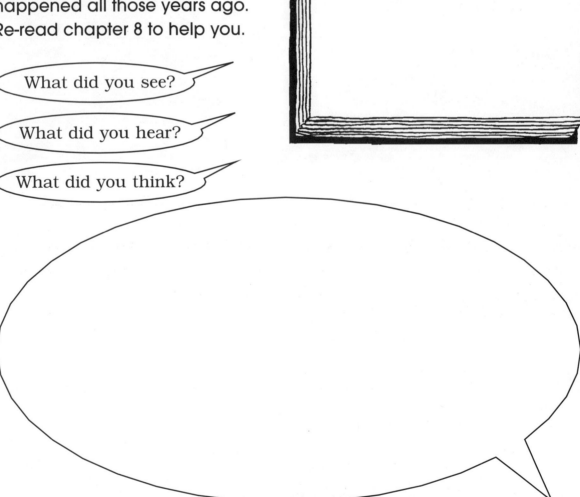

What did you see?

What did you hear?

What did you think?

The bully

● Read Chapter 9.

A lot of stories look at bullying. This may be because so many of us have to deal with the problem.

Ruskin is bullied by Elvis Cave.

● Find the parts of the book where Ruskin has to deal with Elvis Cave. (Look again at Chapters 1, 4, 7 and 9.)

● If you had seen these things happening, what would you have said to Ruskin? Write a letter to Ruskin to help him cope with the situation. You will need to think about these questions:
● *How can your letter support him?*
● *Can you give him any advice?*
● *How do you think it feels to be bullied?*

The death of Corky

● Read Chapter 10. This is one of the saddest parts of the book.

Ruskin finds out what has happened to Corky. Corky is a very special character in the story.

● Without looking in the book, make a list of things you can remember about Corky. Write them in the spaces below.

● Ask some other members of your class for their most important memory of Corky.

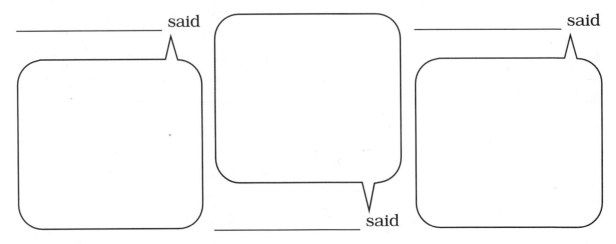

_____ said

_____ said

_____ said

● One thing that still hasn't been explained is the medal. Have you any ideas about how Corky may have won the medal?

RAAAAAHHHHH!

'RAAAAAHHHHH!'
Ruskin froze.
He heard the sound of splashing getting closer.

● Read Chapter 14 – but don't read any further.

● What do you think is going to happen next? Write down what you think will happen to:

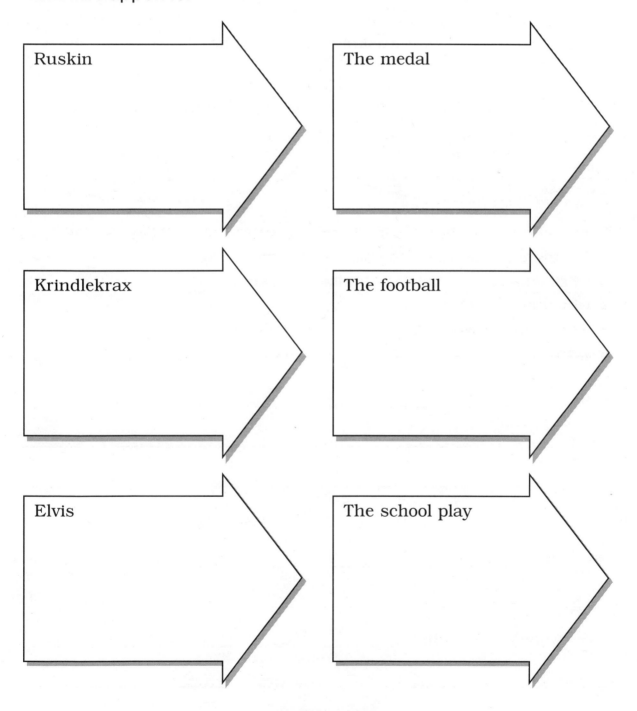

Ruskin

The medal

Krindlekrax

The football

Elvis

The school play

Was it just a dream?

● Read on to the end of the story.

Was Ruskin's meeting with Krindlekrax just a dream, or did it really happen? Here's what some different children have said about it:

'Elvis was there, and that's how he caught a cold.'

'If it was a dream, he would have fallen asleep.'

'If Ruskin didn't meet the crocodile, what happened to that baby crocodile?'

'If there really was a crocodile, it would have eaten Ruskin.'

'It really happened because Ruskin feels better afterwards.'

Can you decide what you think and persuade others? Discuss it with some friends, then fill in the spaces below to explain:
● what you think about the meeting with Krindlekrax;
● why you think that;
● what a friend who disagrees with you thinks;
● what you think about his or her opinion.

I think _____

_____

because _____

_____

My friend says _____

_____

but I would answer that _____

_____

Flashbacks

Sometimes a story is interrupted by a smaller story, which tells you about events that happened before the events in the main story. This is sometimes called a flashback, because it is like a memory in a film: it 'flashes back' to events from the past.

There are several flashbacks in *Krindlekrax*. Each flashback explains something important.

● Re-read the chapter listed in each arrow, and use it to explain the important point written in the arrow.

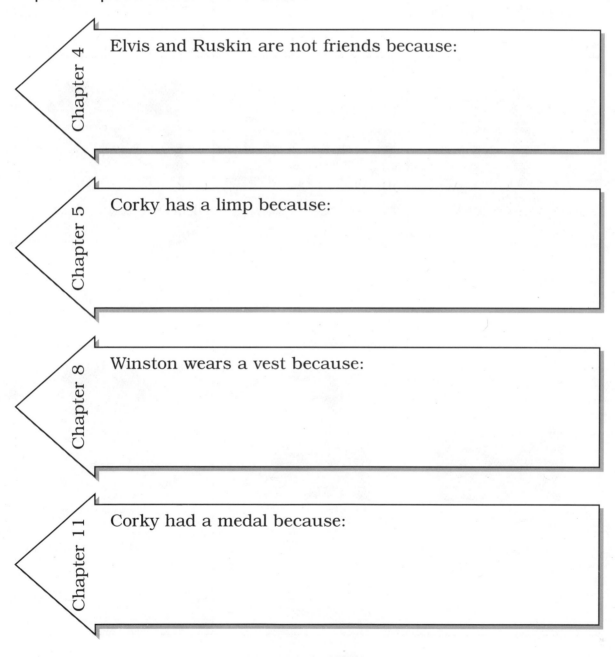

Chapter 4
Elvis and Ruskin are not friends because:

Chapter 5
Corky has a limp because:

Chapter 8
Winston wears a vest because:

Chapter 11
Corky had a medal because:

Chapter pictures

Illustrations can guide a reader. The little picture above the start of each chapter of *Krindlekrax* is linked to what happens in the chapter.

● Explain what each of these pictures shows and how it links to the chapter.

1	2	

3	4	5

6	7	8

Lizard Street people

In Chapter 11, the adults of Lizard Street come to visit Ruskin.

● Imagine you are making a film of this scene. First, re-read Chapter 11 carefully. Then plan your ideas below.

To shoot this scene for your film, you need to think about:
● the set design (where the scene happens);
● the cast (who is in the scene);
● the script (what the characters in the scene say).

Set design
What does Ruskin's room look like? Draw a diagram of the setting.

Cast list
List all the characters in this scene. Which film or TV actors and actresses might play them?

Script
Make notes on the dialogue. Who speaks? What are the main things they say?

Lizard Street people (cont.)

DEVELOPING IDEAS

Here is a shooting script (with setting, actions and dialogue) for an earlier scene from *Krindlekrax – the Movie*:

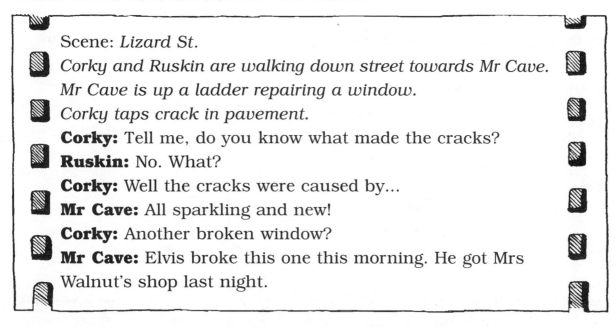

Scene: *Lizard St.*
Corky and Ruskin are walking down street towards Mr Cave.
Mr Cave is up a ladder repairing a window.
Corky taps crack in pavement.
Corky: Tell me, do you know what made the cracks?
Ruskin: No. What?
Corky: Well the cracks were caused by…
Mr Cave: All sparkling and new!
Corky: Another broken window?
Mr Cave: Elvis broke this one this morning. He got Mrs Walnut's shop last night.

● Now draft your own shooting script for the scene described in Chapter 11. Remember to include the setting and actions as well as the dialogue. Continue on the back of this sheet.

● You could go on to plan other parts of your scene. What about adding:
- ● Sound effects?
- ● A poster for your film?
- ● Music?
- ● A storyboard showing some images?

A chain of events

Stories are made when events lead to other events. A chain of events in a story is called a plot.

● Think of the five most important events in *Krindlekrax*. Describe and draw them in the 'plot boxes' below. Make sure you put them in the right order – as they happen in the story.

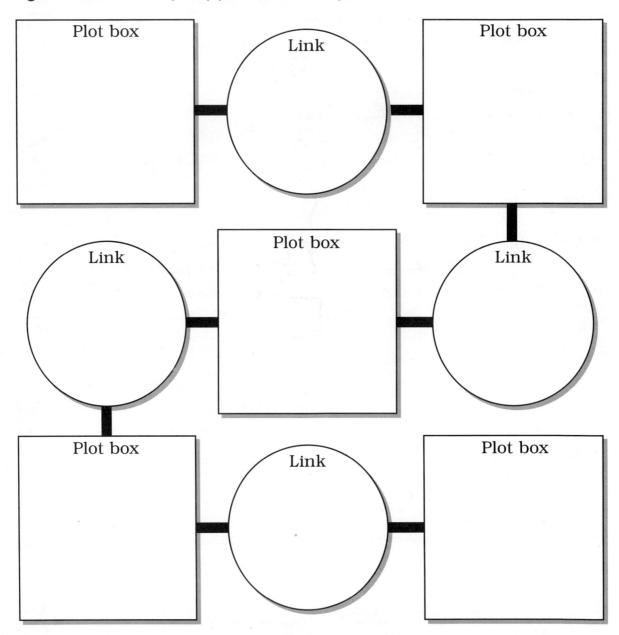

● Think about the links between these events. Did one event cause another? Did one event solve a problem caused by another event?

●Write the links in the bubbles between the plot boxes.

Face to face

In *Krindlekrax*, a lot of different characters talk to each other. But what do they think of each other?

● Look at the pairs below and fill in the 'thought bubbles'. If you are not sure what one character feels about another, try to guess!

Sparky is

Elvis is

Elvis is

Mr Lace is

Mr Cave is

Winston Splinter is

Ruskin is

Mr Lace is

Ruskin is

Mrs Walnut is

Sounds of the street

● Do these sounds remind you of particular objects or characters in *Krindlekrax*? Some are things people say; some are just noises. Find each sound in the book and write down who or what makes it.

Eeeek!
_____

It's not my fault.
_____

Polly-wolly-doodle-all-the-day.
_____

Ka-klunk!
_____

Da-boing!
_____

Yes, sir.
_____

My dear boy...
_____

RAAAAAHHHHH!
_____

TISHOO!
_____

What if...?

In a story like *Krindlekrax*, lots of things happen. These events cause other things to happen. One thing causing another is what gives a story its plot. If certain events didn't happen, the story would be very different.

● Look back through the story and think how different it would be if the following things hadn't happened. Write down the difference you think it would make.

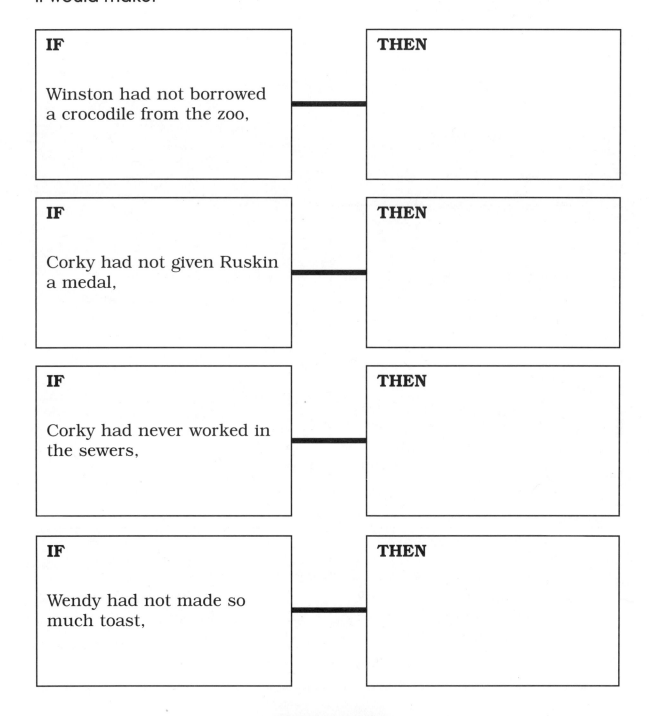

IF	**THEN**
Winston had not borrowed a crocodile from the zoo,	

IF	**THEN**
Corky had not given Ruskin a medal,	

IF	**THEN**
Corky had never worked in the sewers,	

IF	**THEN**
Wendy had not made so much toast,	

When did it happen?

● Cut out the events in the boxes and arrange them in the order in which they happened. Refer to the book if you need to.

Ruskin burst the ball.	Corky found a crocodile in the sewers.
Elvis stole the ball from Ruskin.	Ruskin was born.
Ruskin met Corky for the first time.	Elvis found out about 'Shakespearing' Mr Lace.
Corky found a bomb.	Corky was given a medal.
Ruskin dropped Corky's stick down the drain.	Corky gave the medal to Ruskin.

Looking at Philip Ridley's books

● Read these passages from two other books by Philip Ridley. What similarities can you find between these four passages and parts of *Krindlekrax*? Write on the back of this sheet.

1. Filly and Fergal from *Meteorite Spoon*:

Filly was ten years old, had a shaggy mop of black hair, large, dark eyes and was both very tall and very thin... Fergal, her brother, was seven years old and, although he had a shaggy mop of black hair and large dark eyes, he was the opposite of his sister in almost every other way.

2. Dakota has a scary encounter in *Dakota of the White Flats*:

A noise!
Dakota spun round.
A noise. A noise from behind the armchair!
A strange, scraping sound.
The monster!
Dakota was so scared she couldn't move...
More scraping.
Then she saw it.

3. Miss Whisper gives Filly and Fergal the meteorite spoon:

'Some of the molten metal from the meteor must have covered a kitchen spoon. And this is it! I've kept it on me all these long years. And now... now I'm giving it to you, my very special chicklings.'

'But..: why?' asked Filly.

4. Medusa has lost something:

'It's gone!' cried Medusa breathlessly. 'Gone!'

'What's gone?' asked Dakota...

'The turtle!' screamed Medusa. 'My Oscar has been stolen and it's all your fault, Dakota Pink! It's all your fault!'

How people change

● Think about Ruskin and Elvis at the end of the story. How have they changed since the beginning?

● Re-read Chapters 1 and 17. Write some notes on the chart below to show how the two characters have changed.

Ruskin

Start of story	End of story

Elvis

Start of story	End of story

● On the back of this sheet, write about:
● what made these two characters change;
● what you think about these changes;
● what you liked about other parts of the story.

USING THIS BOOK

Krindlekrax is an urban fantasy. In this novel, the reader finds an inner-city street peopled by classic characters, the central one being a boy called Ruskin Splinter. The story is very visual (Philip Ridley is also an artist and film-maker), with a wonderful use of dialogue and gripping suspense. Through the involving story of a troubled community, the book develops a wide range of emotions. There is fear, grief, jealousy – the lot! This short, rich novel is fast becoming a modern classic.

ORGANIZING THE READING OF *KRINDLEKRAX*

The children should think about the first two activities before reading the book. Page 3 introduces the author, and the first **Ways in** activity (page 4) looks at the impressions gathered from the cover. The 'What is a hero?' activity (page 5) is designed to be done as the children read the opening of the story. Because of the crucial importance of setting in this story, there is a final **Ways in** activity that looks at Lizard Street. This could be discussed before or during the early stages of reading, and returned to later.

The activities in the **Making sense** section are designed to fall in with the reading of the story. Each activity relates to the reading of a chapter or group of chapters, as follows:

- chapter 1 – page 7;
- chapters 2 to 4 – page 8;
- chapter 5 – page 9;
- chapters 6 to 8 – page 10;
- chapter 9 – page 11;
- chapter 10 – page 12;
- chapters 11 to 14 – page 13;
- chapters 15 to 17 – page 14.

The **Developing ideas** activities prompt the children to look back over the whole story. They are asked to re-read specific passages and to explore key themes, as well as becoming aware of the story's narrative structure and distinctive style.

CLASSROOM MANAGEMENT AND SUPPORT

Krindlekrax should ideally be read to the whole class, making the most of the suspense within the story. However, once certain chapters have been read in this way, others could be used for group reading, supported by activities in this book.

The following activities are best worked on by pairs of children: 'Face to face' (page 21); 'When did it happen?' (page 24). The following activities are best done by children working in small groups: 'The death of Corky' (page 12); 'Was it just a dream?' (page 14). The rest can be worked on individually, or with some collaboration.

Activities which require the children to read or re-read a particular part of the book are marked with the icon 📖. It is advisable to invest in at least six copies of the novel, so that groups and pairs can work independently. If the whole class is working on the book, plan for some children to work on activities that require copies of the book while the others are working on activities that do not require direct access to the text. Make sure that you give children ample opportunity to share and discuss their work, in groups or as a class.

DIFFERENTIATION

There is no need for the children to work slavishly through all of the activities in order. Some of the **Making sense** activities might be better left until the children have finished reading *Krindlekrax*.

All of the activities are aimed at Years 3 and 4 of the primary school, and will also prove useful with Year 5 and Year 6 classes. Teachers will need to plan to support children who may

struggle with some of the material. The core learning objective of each activity is stated (as its **Aim**) in the Teachers' notes on pages 29–32. Different children will achieve these aims to varying degrees.

Some of the more challenging activities are: 'Meet the Splinters' (page 7), 'In the sewers' (page 9), 'RAAAAAHHHHH!' (page 13), 'Flashbacks' (page 15), 'Face to face' (page 21) and 'What if...?' (page 23).

TIME-SCALE

Krindlekrax can be read within a week: some classes have managed this, with extra story times slotted in here and there. However, the activities in this book should encourage the reading of the story to be stretched over a longer period of time. The activities provide material for reflection on the story and involve recall of particular events, helping the children to maintain their grasp of the storyline.

LIZARD STREET KIDS

Krindlekrax is a tried and tested hit with children at Key Stage 2. Ideally, it should be read and reflected on over a period of time; this will help the children to absorb its style and message, giving it a degree of 'cult status' in the class. Children recognize the story's frustrated hero, unhappy bully, nervous parents and long-suffering neighbours as comic but relevant versions of familiar realities.

TEACHING POTENTIAL OF KRINDLEKRAX

The **Extensions** suggested in the Teachers' notes on pages 30-32 indicate some of the potential that this text has for further work in English. The story's emphasis on the local history and geography of Lizard Street create the potential for cross-curricular work; for example, the text could stimulate children to explore the history of their own street or district. Lizard Street contains a wealth of oral tradition, and children could use this as a stimulus to explore oral narrative in their own locality.

There is also much potential for work on personal and social education linked to the theme of bullying. *Krindlekrax* explores not only the effect of bullying on victims but the behaviour of witnesses and a bully's ally, and even suggests some possible reasons for bullying.

In addition, *Krindlekrax* can be used as a springboard for work on media awareness. Philip Ridley is a screen writer and director, and the visual aspect of his work shines through this story. Its sharply-paced scenes and dialogue can provide an excellent stimulus for drama activities in which children act out or improvise scenes based on the story.

RECOMMENDED PREVIOUS TEACHING

These activities will work well if the children:
- can read and write independently;
- can scan a text for information;
- can express and justify opinions;
- are used to discussing stories;
- can empathize with the feelings of characters in stories;
- have encountered other stories with which they can compare this one.

LITERARY TERMS

During the activities in this book, the following terms are used repeatedly:
- story structure;
- plot;
- character;
- setting.

These terms will need to be discussed, and the children will need to be reminded of their meaning. Each of these terms is discussed more fully in *Reading and responding to fiction* by Huw Thomas (see 'Further reading' below).

FURTHER READING

The following resources will be useful to support work with *Krindlekrax*.

Other books by Philip Ridley
Mercedes Ice (Puffin)
Dakota of the White Flats (Puffin)
Meteorite Spoon (Puffin)
Kasper in the Glitter (Puffin)
Scribbleboy (Puffin)
ZinderZunder (Puffin)
Two Plays for Young People: Fairytaleheart and Sparkleshark (Faber & Faber)

Other urban fantasies
The Third Class Genie by Robert Leeson (Collins)
The Secret of Platform 13 by Eva Ibbotson (Macmillan)
A Razzle Dazzle Rainbow by Chris Powling (Puffin)
Maniac Magee by Jerry Spinelli (Hippo)
Maphead by Lesley Howarth (Walker)
Harvey Angell by Diana Hendry (Red Fox)

Other books dealing with bullying
The Eighteenth Emergency by Betsy Byars (Red Fox)
Chicken by Alan Gibbons (Dent)

For teachers
The ideas of story structure, plot and character are dealt with in *Reading and Responding to Fiction: Classroom Strategies for Developing Literacy* by Huw Thomas (Scholastic).

Krindlekrax

TEACHERS' NOTES

INTRODUCTION
WORDS FROM THE AUTHOR

Aim: to relate an author's comments to the style and content of a book.

Teaching points: it might be worth enlarging this page to A3 size and displaying it, so the children can refer to these quotes more easily. As the class progresses through the story, it is worth pausing every so often to re-read the quotes and ask the class for their thoughts on what Ridley has said. Certain aspects of the story tie in with his comments – for example, Ruskin's love of Lizard Street (see Chapter 1 of Krindlekrax) fits in with Ridley's observation about the beauty of 'a run-down street'.

Extension: children could look at newspapers, TV guides and magazines to find out about the ideas that inspire and motivate other creative artists. Interviews in music or film magazines can be used to build up a collection of quotes.

WAYS IN
LOOKING AT THE COVER

Aim: to understand the different features of a book cover and how they affect the reader.

Teaching points: the sheet can be given to the children along with copies of the book. They can thus match the features on the diagram with those on the actual cover.

Extension: children could identify the same features on other book covers, and make notes of the questions prompted by these covers (as on the sheet). They could also evaluate the effectiveness of particular covers: can they find a 'bad' example of a book cover, and explain why it 'doesn't work'?

WHAT IS A HERO?

Aim: to investigate how characters are portrayed in stories.

Teaching points: prompt the children to itemise the conventional features of a 'hero' or 'heroine', bearing in mind that the purpose of this exercise is to draw out some of the varied images these terms can evoke. It may be worth having some current 'hero' figures in mind (from sport, TV series and so on) with which to prompt the children's thoughts. The children's pictures and descriptions of heroic figures can be collected and displayed.

Extension: children could look for other unusual heroic figures in stories – for example, Babe in *The Sheep-Pig* by Dick King-Smith (Puffin).

LIZARD STREET

Aim: to monitor the use of a setting in a story. Teaching points: as they read the story, the children will encounter particular incidents or passages involving the labelled features on this map. It might be worth enlarging the map to A3 size and displaying it where the children can see and discuss it. As the story unfolds, objects on the landscape such as the drain and the pub sign take on a particular significance.

Extension: children could design their own setting for a story, perhaps drawing on features of their own locality.

The idea of local myths and legends could also be explored. Do the children know any 'tall tales' from the streets or districts where they live? Suitable anecdotes could be recorded on cassette. It may be possible to ask adults from the local community to visit the school and recount some strange tales.

MAKING SENSE
MEET THE SPLINTERS

Aim: to investigate how characters are portrayed in stories.

Teaching points: this activity helps the children to recognize three of the most significant ways in which readers gather impressions of characters in stories – through description of their external appearance, their speech and their actions.

Extension: children could use the questions in this activity to build up a profile of another character in another story.

BUILDING THE SUSPENSE

Aim: to understand how story events can be used to build up suspense.

Teaching points: suspense occurs when the author plays on the reader's sense of expectation. We expect to learn the answers to Corky's questions, but they keep on being delayed. This activity develops the children's awareness of suspense as an aspect of story structure.

Extension: children could look at other examples of suspense in stories or films. In each case, they are looking for the same two essential elements: something that is expected, and a means by which it is delayed.

IN THE SEWERS

Aim: to investigate the use of setting in a story.

Teaching points: as in 'What is a hero?' (page 5), this activity can highlight a contrast between reader expectations and what the text actually depicts. Seen through Corky's eyes, the sewers are 'beautiful' and 'majestic'.

Many other stories have used the sewers for a setting. Novels such as *The Phantom of the Opera* by Gaston Leroux (Penguin), films such as *The Third Man* and television programmes such as *Teenage Mutant Ninja Turtles* have drawn on this evocative location. The idea of a set of connected passages running underneath our everyday world is a powerful one.

Extension: children could draw the sewer setting for *Krindlekrax*, using ideas from the text. Can they make the sewer look as wonderful as Corky makes it out to be? Could they design a sewer setting for a story of their own?

WHAT HAPPENED THAT NIGHT?

Aim: to understand the ways in which a story can be told from different characters' viewpoints.

Teaching points: as an introduction to the activity, it may be worth asking the children to pretend that they are characters from the story. Individuals can then be 'hot-seated': asked to sit facing the rest of the class, pretending that they are particular characters from the pub scene in Chapter 8. The rest of the class then ask them questions about that night, and they answer as their chosen characters would.

Extension: children might like to contrast two possible versions of the crocodile story, asking questions such as *Who made the biggest mistake?* and *Why did things go wrong?*

THE BULLY

Aim: to consider issues raised in a story.

Teaching points: this part of the novel confronts the children with a difficulty they may have experienced. You will need to handle discussion of Ruskin's experience of bullying with sensitivity. Discussion could focus on questions such as *Why do you think bullies do what they do?* and *What is the best way to deal with a bully?*

Extension: children could produce their own pieces of writing or drama on the theme of bullying. They could try, in their stories, to provide solutions to the problems they describe.

THE DEATH OF CORKY

Aim: to empathize with the feelings of characters in a story.

Teaching points: the children can use this activity to look back at the character of Corky and consider his contribution to the story. They could cut out thought-shaped bubbles and write their thoughts about Corky inside them. The collected thoughts could then be displayed.

Extension: children could look at how the previous chapter prepared them for the news of Corky's death. Why might Corky have felt so tired? What do the children feel on re-reading

the words 'It could wait until tomorrow' just before the end of Chapter 9?

RAAAAAHHHHH!

Aim: to explore the structure of narrative by making and testing predictions.

Teaching points: prediction is an essential aspect of the way in which readers keep track of their understanding of a story. Through asking questions and focusing on the children's varied responses, you should be able to gather a wide variety of suggestions about what will happen; this variety should be emphasized to the children.

Extension: children could be given books and short stories which are unfamiliar to them, and set the task of reading to a particular point and predicting how the story will end.

WAS IT JUST A DREAM?

Aim: to consider what is 'real' and 'imaginary' within the context of a story.

Teaching points: a class of children reading *Krindlekrax* tend to end up debating whether the crocodile 'really' came out of the sewer, or whether it was 'really' just a dream. The children should accept that the question remains open: it cannot be resolved with certainty. The comments quoted on the sheet are fairly typical of the points that tend to be made in discussion. Encourage the children to respond specifically to each other's arguments, rather than simply repeating their own views.

Extension: children could look back through the whole story and consider how plausible all the events are. Is the story realistic or fantastic? What is the boundary between one and the other?

DEVELOPING IDEAS
FLASHBACKS

Aim: to explore the ordering of events in a narrative.

Teaching points: flashbacks often appear in stories to explain the current situation represented in the narrative. They step outside of the chronological time followed by the story. This activity helps the children to understand the explanatory function of flashbacks. The term 'flashbacks' referred originally to films; but similar stories-within-stories are a feature of many older narratives.

Extension: children could look at the use of flashbacks in some traditional stories, such as 'The Frog Prince'.

CHAPTER PICTURES

Aim: to identify and follow the main features of a novel-length storyline.

Teaching points: one of the key skills that children should develop in their work with novels is the ability to understand and recall the overall storyline. In this activity, the pictures which start off the individual chapters are used as prompts to help the children develop their memory of the whole story. In some cases, the children will need to think carefully in order to work out who is featured in the picture (for example, the picture for Chapter 11 is presumably of Mrs Walnut).

Extension: children could be asked to invent an alternative set of chapter pictures, draw them and explain how they are linked to the text.

LIZARD STREET PEOPLE

Aim: to identify and consider significant characters; to consider characters, setting and dialogue in order to write a film script.

Teaching points: provide additional paper for this activity. Looking at Chapter 11 should lead the children to think about the behaviour and speech of the main characters from Lizard Street. In planning their film scene, they will need to consider how they can show what the characters are thinking and feeling. They will also have to decide how to include the story of Corky and

the unexploded bomb. Will they have this story recounted in speech or shown as a flashback? Their script should draw on the ideas they developed in planning the scene.

Extension: children could draw a storyboard to show the action in this chapter as a sequence of frames. Encourage them to consider the use of close-ups, different camera angles and so on.

A CHAIN OF EVENTS

Aim: to understand the way in which events cause other events in the plot of a story.

Teaching points: the key teaching point in this lesson is the explanation of a narrative plot as a causal chain of events (one event causing another). Any significant point in the story could be looked at to identify the event that is taking place, how other events have caused it to happen and how this event then leads to further events.

Extension: children could try using the idea of plot boxes to plan their own simple stories, devising one event that leads to another and so on. Encourage them to see that such a chain of events can create tension and momentum in a story – like the toppling of a row of dominoes!

FACE TO FACE

Aim: to discuss the feelings of characters and how they respond to each other.

Teaching points: it is essential to make the purpose of this activity clear to the children. They are not being asked to state their own feelings about any particular character. They are being asked to get inside the skin of a particular character and express that person's feelings towards another character in the story.

Extension: the names of the characters could be written on slips of paper, each child drawing a name out of a hat. They could then work in pairs, each child trying to state how her/his character might feel about the character her/his partner has drawn. Ask them to find evidence in the text for believing that a character would think or feel in a particular way.

SOUNDS OF THE STREET

Aim: to investigate the use of language for effect in a story.

Teaching points: the children should initially try to attribute the noises and phrases on the sheet to particular objects or people without looking at the text. Some children may need recourse to the book. Through discussion, the children can explore the effect of the repetition of these sounds: how the sounds give the reader a clear impression of characters and places; how they create tension; how they remind the reader of past events; and so on.

Extension: children could try using distinctive noises and catchphrases in their own stories. They could start with a list of sounds and phrases, then devise a story to include them.

WHAT IF...?

Aim: to develop children's awareness of plot in stories.

Teaching points: before trying this activity, it might be worth asking some other *What if?* questions that are closer to home – for example, *What if a flood happened and the whole of our area was under a metre of water?* This will help them to consider the implications of changes in the storyline, and thus to appreciate how the events are connected.

Extension: children could look back through the story and suggest further **What if...** puzzles. This requires them to identify points where, had something happened differently, the future course of the story would have changed. They could look for examples of such 'turning points' or 'crossroads' in other stories.

WHEN DID IT HAPPEN?

Aim: to explore the ways in which a narrative can be ordered.

Teaching points: this activity can result in an interesting confusion. In chronological terms, the first event on the sheet is 'Corky found a bomb.' This happened before any of the other events. However, in the book, this episode is told in Chapter 11. The children should arrange the event boxes in the order in which things happened; this activity thus helps them to see how narrative order can differ from chronological order. If necessary, remind them about 'flashbacks' (see Teachers' notes for page 15).

Extension: children can use two copies of page 24 to arrange the events in two lines, one showing the chronological order and the other showing the narrative order. Comparing these two lines will tell them a lot about the author's storytelling method.

LOOKING AT PHILIP RIDLEY'S BOOKS

Aim: to compare different works by the same author, looking for similar features.

Teaching points: the reading of *Krindlekrax* should stimulate the children to look for other books by Philip Ridley. You can use this activity to recommend the two novels quoted from – and perhaps others too! The chief similarities the children should identify are as follows:
• The character descriptions of Filly and Fergal can be compared with those of the Splinters in Chapter 1 of *Krindlekrax*.
• The suspense of the 'A noise!' scene can be compared with the approach of Krindlekrax.
• Miss Whisper's gift to Filly and Fergal can be compared with Corky's gift to Ruskin.
• The loss of Medusa's turtle can be compared with Winston's loss of the baby crocodile.

Extension: children could read another Ridley novel and compare the events, characters and style of writing with those in *Krindlekrax*.

EVALUATION
HOW PEOPLE CHANGE

Aim: to investigate the changing nature of characters; to assess the content and appeal of a story.

Teaching points: through this activity, the children will develop an overview of the story's content. Through discussion, help them to think about the reasons why Ruskin and Elvis change in the course of the story. This will help them to assess the story and focus their personal responses to it.

Extension: children could draw two parallel lines on a sheet of paper, labelling one line 'Ruskin' and the other 'Elvis'. They could then mark between the lines the various points at which the two characters meet, and add brief comments summarizing what each character was like at that point in the story.

CDM Regulations 2015 Procedures Manual

CDM Regulations 2015 Procedures Manual

Fourth Edition

STUART D. SUMMERHAYES
BSc, MSc, IFaPS

WILEY Blackwell

First edition published 2005
Second edition published 2011
Third edition published 2016

Registered Office
John Wiley & Sons, Ltd, The Atrium, Southern Gate, Chichester, West Sussex, PO19 8SQ, United Kingdom

Editorial Offices
9600 Garsington Road, Oxford, OX4 2DQ, United Kingdom
The Atrium, Southern Gate, Chichester, West Sussex, PO19 8SQ, United Kingdom

For details of our global editorial offices, for customer services and for information about how to apply for permission to reuse the copyright material in this book please see our website at www.wiley.com/wiley-blackwell.

Library of Congress Cataloging-in-Publication Data

Names: Summerhayes, Stuart, author.
Title: CDM regulations 2015 : procedures manual / Stuart Summerhayes.
Description: Fourth edition. | Hoboken : John Wiley & Sons Inc., 2016. | Includes bibliographical references and index.
Identifiers: LCCN 2016010484 | ISBN 9781119243038 (pbk.) | ISBN 9781119243083 (epub)
Subjects: LCSH: Construction industry–Safety regulations–Great Britain.
Classification: LCC KD3172.C6 S86 2016 | DDC 343.4107/8624–dc22
LC record available at http://lccn.loc.gov/2016010484

A catalogue record for this book is available from the British Library.

Wiley also publishes its books in a variety of electronic formats. Some content that appears in print may not be available in electronic books.

Cover image: Gettyimages/urfinguss

Set in 10/13pt Franklin Gothic by SPi Global, Pondicherry, India
Printed and bound in Malaysia by Vivar Printing Sdn Bhd

1 2016

Contents

Acknowledgements

I would like to dedicate this book to the memory of my mother Violet May, to my daughters Emma and Kate, and in acknowledgement of the constant support and encouragement of my wife, Linda, without whom it would never have been completed.

1 Introduction

The third version of the Construction (Design and Management) Regulations was published twenty years after the original version (31 March 1995) became part of the construction industry's legislative framework. The interim period has also seen the publication of the second version on the 6 April 2007.This development route has attracted criticism at every stage, partly from dissatisfaction with some of the legal requirements, partly from a lack of managerial judgment and partly from self-interest, to the detriment of regulatory achievement.

The Regulations, as always, attempt to endorse the holistic, team-based approach for the effective delivery of construction health and safety management, within a dynamic and often fragmented construction industry. Successful delivery is dependent upon the concept of shared objectives, delivered through dutyholder integration, but such success is constantly challenged by the disparate nature of construction teams and the disenfranchisement that often exists.

Whilst this third version of the Regulations has been drafted to account for a closer alignment with the original European Directive, it also embraces a response to the criticism collated by the corresponding panels associated with the reviews of the two previous versions of the Regulations. It is prudent to highlight some of these criticisms so that their messages are not lost and so that the spectral focus of future concerns is directed elsewhere. Many of the criticisms remain as challenges in respect of all future dutyholder management models.

The following tabulation provides an insight into the salient issues that must be addressed so that the 'best practice model' can indeed signal progression.

Critical point	Commentary
• added value	failure to articulate the value of service provision
• bureaucracy	generation of excessive and irrelevant paperwork
• communication	ineffective; lack of meaningful dialogue
• dutyholder invisibility	lack of dutyholder presence within the project team
• generic approaches	absence of a project-specific focus
• inflexibility	lack of appreciation that numerous options exist as evidence of the discharge of duties
• interpretation	dogmatic mis-interpretation of Regulations
• intransigence	the inability to appreciate valid arguments

(Continued)

Critical point	Commentary
• non-integration	inability to function as a team member
• philosophical alignment	failure to appreciate underlying principles
• process ignorance	mis-understanding of design and construction processes
• third party appointments	additional and unnecessary resource cost

Further insights into the underlying tensions within the construction industry can be gained from the two seminal reports of the 1990s, namely the Latham Report[1] and the subsequent Egan Report.[2] Both were designed to strategically position the construction industry for the challenges of the new millennium and to simultaneously provoke debate on the future direction of the industry. Change was demanded as a factor of competitiveness and economic viability, and promoted on the concepts of partnering, risk management and the integrated team ethos. Whilst the more enlightened moved with aspirational intent, others peddled the concepts without conviction or philosophical commitment, and subsequently targets remained largely undelivered. Thus, change has always proved challenging and will continue to do so.

The 'Collaboration for Change'[3] report provides the following insight on industry reform:

> Few in the industry believe that it is organised in a way that works well for clients and the full depth of the supply chain. There is little or no integration between design, product manufacture, construction, operation and asset management; no feedback loop that increases the chances of a completed asset performing as it should, and of future projects learning from the past; and no alignment of interests within the supply chain and between the supply chain and the client. This fragmentation of interests destroys value.

These identifiable characteristics represent indicators of entrenchment and resistance, which, unless dismantled, remain as barriers to progress and restrain the possibility of achievement of 'best practice' standards and the symbiotic relationship between project and health and safety success.

The philosophical foundations of project management address the criticisms above, and provide the bedrock for asset delivery improvement via the integrated team, through effective communication and cooperation. These are relevant perspectives for the construction industry in the general sense and for the delivery of health and safety outcomes compliant with the Regulations in the specific sense. The Regulations are one more stage in the evolution of construction-related legislation, traceable back to the Health and Safety at Work etc. Act 1974 (H & S W Act 1974).[4]

This Act represented the culmination of the findings from the Robens Report of 1972,[5] which was charged with appraising the state of workplace legislation and providing direction for long overdue improvements across many sectors of industry. It expressed concern over and identified such issues as: a lack of coherence in the way existing laws had been drafted; reliance on implementation by the factory inspectorate; failure to keep pace with technological advancements and the lack of inclusion of the health and education sectors.

---

[1] *Constructing the Team*, The Latham Report, HMSO, July 1994. ISBN 9780117529946.
[2] *Rethinking Construction*, The Egan Report, HMSO, November 1998. ISBN 9780632059287.
[3] *Collaboration for Change*, The Edge Commission Report on the Future of Professionalism, Edge, May 2015. ISBN 9780993249709.
[4] The Health and Safety at Work etc. Act 1974, July 1974, HMSO.
[5] The Robens Report, Lord Robens, June 1972.

These findings initiated the subsequent launch of the H & S W Act 1974, which remains the primary piece of legislation covering occupational health and safety in Great Britain.

The Act changed the face of workplace legislation and championed the concept of health and safety responsibility for those who controlled and contributed within the workplace environment. It is sometimes referred to as an empowering Act, and gave rise to:

- the Health and Safety Commission[6]

- the Health and Safety Executive

- the formation of the Employment and Medical Advisory Service (EMAS)

- the publication of Approved Codes of Practice and Guidance Notes, and

- a mechanism by which secondary legislation could get onto the statute books without going through the full time-consuming parliamentary process.

This Act established the 'duty of care' to be exercised towards all those affected by the work outcomes of the relevant industries and established a 'deemed to satisfy' approach based on 'management by objectives' and the avoidance of prescriptive legislation.

This modernisation process was further accelerated through membership of the European Union and its harmonisation policy, via associated European Directives. Such Directives require member states to introduce their own legislation to achieve the objectives set out in the relevant Directive. Their purpose is to achieve compatibility of legal outcomes across all member states, with each member state having flexibility of interpretation in respect of its mechanism for delivery.

Directive 89/391 EEC[7] gave rise in the UK to the following six workplace regulations:

- Management of Health and Safety at Work Regulations (1992, now 1999)

- Provision and Use of Work Equipment Regulations (1992, now 1998)

- Manual Handling Operations Regulations (1992)

- Workplace (Health, Safety and Welfare) Regulations (1992)

- Personal Protective Equipment Regulations (1992)

- Health and Safety (Display Screen Equipment) Regulations (1992).

Although all the above have impacted on working lives, it was the Management of Health and Safety at Work Regulations (1992) that first introduced the legal requirement of the risk assessment approach, which was fundamental to the development of hazard identification and workplace method statements.

Regulation 3 states that

> Every employer shall make a suitable and sufficient assessment of—
>
> (a) the risks to the health and safety of his employees to which they are exposed whilst they are at work; and
>
> (b) the risks to the health and safety of persons not in his employment arising out of or in connection with the conduct by him of his undertaking, for the purpose of identifying the measures he needs to take to comply with the requirements and prohibitions imposed upon him by or under the relevant statutory provisions and by Part II of the Fire Precautions (Workplace) Regulations 1997.

---

[6] The HSC and HSE merged on the 1 April 2008 into one unified body, the Health and Safety Executive (HSE).

[7] European Framework Directive on Safety and Health at Work.

A similar duty is placed on the self-employed.

Thus the concept of risk assessment has been part of statutory duty since 1 January 1993, and through the associated 'general principles of prevention' forms the key management response underpinning the various versions of the CDM Regulations.

Construction-related legislative development continued with European Directive 92/57, 'Temporary or Mobile Construction Sites'. This was passed on the 24 June 1992, and required the implementation of minimum health and safety measures to prevent risks on civil engineering and building sites by establishing a chain of responsibility for all parties involved. It also linked with the relevant provisions of Directive 89/391 EEC, 'the Framework Directive',[8] and imposed a deadline of 31 December 1993 for transposition by member states.

In principle, this Directive identified the role and responsibilities of:

- client
- supervisor
- coordinator
- notification
- health and safety plan
- file for future work

and endorsed the requirements for

- cooperation and coordination
- general principles of prevention
- minimum health and safety goals
- prohibition of entry to the unauthorised
- supply of information to the workforce, and
- consultation with workers and/or their representatives.

The UK's response to the above Directive has been translated into the Construction (Design and Management) Regulations and the Construction (Health, Safety and Welfare) Regulations 1996 (CHSW) (now enshrined in PART 4 of the current Regulations).

The former implements the planning and management aspects of the Directive and the CHSW implements the practical implementation aspects. It is to be noted that the narrative of the Directive has not changed since its launch on 24 June 1993, whilst the CDM Regulations are now in their third version, with each revision attempting to achieve closer alignment with the objectives of the Directive itself.

The journey of legislative development has been varied and often torturous, with the CDM management model intent on continuing with this *journey of constant improvement*, which itself resonates with the key principles of project management. Thus, the career professional will never arrive, but must constantly seek to learn lessons from the last experience to enhance future performance in all areas of project and health and safety construction management.

Complacency must always be challenged and management systems continually reviewed, updated and revised to ensure that controls remain effective and that any

---

[8] Directive 89/391/EEC – OSH Framework Directive, June 1989, introduced measures to encourage improvements in the safety and health of workers at work.

project changes/variations/alterations with a health and safety implication are fully appreciated and due responses undertaken. Such perspectives are evident in dutyholder statutory obligations associated not only with these Regulations but also with all other construction-related legislation.

Successful project outcomes are delivered by the integrated team based on good communication and cooperation, within the embrace of the holistic approach. If there is a problem on a construction site then it has an impact on all parties involved on that site. In the project management sense there is no benefit in the 'blame game' at any project stage, since fragmentation ensures that other agendas persist to the detriment of team deliverables. Furthermore, such fragmentation ensures that *safe* and *suitable* systems of work are likely to be compromised and successful outcomes undermined.

The CDM Regulations 2015 implicitly depend on the integrated team, with many of the philosophical threads described above woven into the associated narrative. In reality there is nothing new in the factors that deliver successful projects, and 'best practice'[9] would indeed have highlighted most of the agenda items. The underlying principles of project management are therefore endorsed through the perspectives associated with dutyholder roles enshrined in these Regulations.

Change must be accommodated and improvements made acknowledging the argument that today's issues stem more from the failure of the construction industry to evolve culturally than from shortcomings in the legislation itself.

Success will only be delivered to the requisite best standard when all team members share the same philosophy and own the means of deliverance, in a mutually appreciative team-based manner. This applies to all aspects of project management, with the underlying philosophy offering a vehicle for delivery. The cultural climate must support this, since reliance on legislation itself will not create the necessary change now expected.

The government rationale for the promotion of these Regulations cites the following objectives: simplification; a reduced level of bureaucracy; regulatory consistency; real risk focus; risk management by risk creators; and retaining responsibility within the supply chain, thus avoiding third party involvement.

Such promotional objectives have now been delivered through:

- Simplification;
- Fewer regulations;
- A team-based and integrated holistic process;
- Critical appointments from within the professional team;
- Closer alignment with the contractual process;
- Promotion of project management principles;
- Key appointments unrelated to notification;
- Greater integrative liaison between principal designer and principal contractor;
- No exemption for domestic clients;
- Removal of direct reference to the Workplace (Health, Safety and Welfare) Regulations 1992;

---

[9] **Note:** Compliance with this and other construction-related legislation remains a bare minimum of performance. A best practice approach could well be set above the minimum level of compliance.

- Competence clarified and now based on skills, knowledge, training and experience as well as organisational capability;

- Document management related to best practice professional standards;

- Greater proactive involvement of the design team (principal designer) in the construction phase plan and the health and safety file.

However, detractors may offer counter-arguments about

- less robust process controls,

- over-reliance on the professional team, together with

- the removal of the CDM coordinator,

all leading to an unsatisfactory overall process.

Despite concerns and counter-arguments, the construction industry must now deliver a compliant response as a bare minimum, and champion, over a period of time, a benchmark standard above this minimum that serves the longer-term aims and aspirations of the industry.

The championing of an improved standard is dependent on cultural change and cannot be perceived as simply aspirational, since health and safety is a factor of statutory provision and criminal law.

* *

Statistically, any improvement in the health and safety aspects of the construction industry can be crudely appreciated by direct reference to the HSE's annual publication of workplace statistics,[10] as correlated by the Office of National Statistics. These annual figures do not account for the level of occupational ill-health associated with the industry's procedures and methodologies, nor can they account for the acknowledged under-reporting of related issues.

The process of reporting occupational ill-health is neither robust nor absolute in terms of accuracy, and any analysis must account for associated discrepancies arising from:

- acknowledged level of under-reporting

- time lapse between ill-health cause and effect

- transient nature of the work-force

- variation in the categorisation of accidents

- changes in reporting procedures over given time periods

- drift of workforce into other industries.

However, improvements can be identified, with the last ratifiable year (up to 31 March 2015) representing the lowest number of construction-related fatalities since records began and the incidence rate being far lower than the 5.5/100,000 workers recorded in the 1990s.

Period	Fatalities	Incidence Rate	Comment
2014/2015	35	1.62/100,000	Lowest number and rate of construction worker deaths on record

---

[10] *Health and Safety Statistics. Annual Report for Great Britain 2014/1*: www.hse.gov.uk

There is much to be pleased about, although the statistics merely provide a limited insight into an ongoing and ever-changing situation of complexity. The CDM Regulations undoubtedly contribute, but cannot be cited as the lone initiator of progress.

The industry owes a debt to the large- to medium-sized contractors, who for some time have appreciated the necessity for health and safety resource compatibility in support of their workforce. Acknowledgement must also be made of the alignment of the design professions over the last twenty years, which has provided greater transparency and illumination of their vital contribution to the Regulations, as well as of those clients who promote best practice and who have the vision and understanding to fully appreciate the influence they are able to exert on the project.

The continuation of this improvement is a necessity to be augmented by the performance of the small to medium construction enterprises that have been targeted by a number of specific legal obligations enshrined in the current changes.

There is still much to be done and this journey of improvement remains a never-ending challenge.

* * * * * * * * * * * * * * * * * * * *

These Regulations are supported by a Guidance Document (L153),[11] unlike the previous versions, which were accompanied by an Approved Code of Practice (ACoP). The guidance document states that:

> Following the guidance is not compulsory, unless specifically stated, and you are free to take other action. But if you do follow the guidance you will normally be doing enough to comply with the law. Health and safety inspectors seek to secure compliance with the law and may refer to this guidance.

This is a lower legal standard than that presented by the previous ACoP, which established a reverse burden of proof requiring the dutyholder to provide evidence of compliance. This evidential trail must still be there but the move from an ACoP to guidance facilitates the drafting of any future amendments into the document itself, with the document intended to be further supported by sectoral guidance. Large sections of the previous ACoP have been taken into the body of the guidance, but not all.

* * * * * * * * * * * * * * * * * * * *

There are many stakeholders on construction projects who do not carry statutory duties, but who nonetheless have an impact, whether positive or negative, on the project. All have to be managed by the project team and particularly by the project manager.

It is imperative that a team ethos dominates the project since it is a fundamental parameter for successful delivery. Fragmentation has no place in the challenging and dynamic construction environment, for it ensures that goals are fudged and attainable objectives masked to the detriment of health and safety as well as other project factors.

The CDM management model must attain more than the sum of its parts, through enhanced levels of communication, cooperation, contribution and coordination aimed at health and safety deliverables.

The CDM Regulations 2015 provides the vehicle for that delivery, driven by the commitment of the construction professional, with failure and non-compliance not options for consideration.

---

[11] *Managing Health and Safety in Construction: Guidance on Regulations*, published by HSE Books. ISBN 9780717666263.

2 Interpretation

For the purpose of these Regulations, relevant work must come under the definition of 'construction of a structure', as defined below (Regulation 2(1): Interpretation):

'[C]onstruction work' means the carrying out of any building, civil engineering or engineering construction work and includes—

(a) the construction, alteration, conversion, fitting out, commissioning, renovation, repair, upkeep, redecoration or other maintenance (including cleaning which involves the use of water or an abrasive at high pressure or the use of corrosive or toxic substances), de-commissioning, demolition or dismantling of a structure;

(b) the preparation for an intended structure, including site clearance, exploration, investigation (but not site survey) and excavation *(but not pre-construction archaeological investigations)*,[1] and the clearance or preparation of the site or structure for use or occupation at its conclusion;

(c) the assembly of prefabricated elements to form a structure or the disassembly on site of prefabricated elements which, immediately before such disassembly, formed a structure;

(d) the removal of a structure or of any product or waste resulting from demolition or dismantling of a structure or from disassembly of prefabricated elements which, immediately before such disassembly, formed such a structure;

(e) the installation, commissioning, maintenance, repair or removal of mechanical, electrical, gas, compressed air, hydraulic, telecommunications, computer or similar services which are normally fixed within or to a structure,

but does not include the exploration for an extraction of mineral resources or preparatory activities carried out at a place where such exploration or extraction is carried out.

'[S]tructure' means—

(a) any building, timber, masonry, metal or reinforced concrete structure, railway line or siding, tramway line, dock, harbour, inland navigation, tunnel, shaft, bridge, viaduct, waterworks, reservoir, pipe or pipeline, cable, aqueduct, sewer, sewage works, gasholder, road, airfield, sea defence works, river works, drainage works, earthworks, lagoon, dam, wall, caisson, mast, tower, pylon, underground tank, earth retaining structure, or structure designed to preserve or alter any natural feature, and fixed plant;

(b) any structure similar to anything specified in paragraph (a);

(c) any formwork, falsework, scaffold or other structure designed or used to provide support or means of access during construction work,

and any reference to a structure includes a part of a structure.

---

[1] Emphasis added. Additional to the previous definition under the CDM Regulations 2007.

CDM Regulations 2015 Procedures Manual, Fourth Edition. Stuart D. Summerhayes.
© 2016 John Wiley & Sons, Ltd. Published 2016 by John Wiley & Sons, Ltd.

Work that does not come under the above definition is not outside the law for it must still comply, where applicable, with other related legislation, for example:

- The Mines and Quarries Act 1954
- The Personal Protective Equipment Regulations 1992
- The Management of Health and Safety at Work Regulations 1999
- The Work at Height Regulations 2005
- The Control of Noise at Work Regulations 2005
- The Offshore Installations Regulations 2015
- etc.

Additionally, the previous ACoP identified the following as 'not construction work as defined' under the CDM Regulations 2007:

- putting up and taking down of marquees and tents
- general maintenance of fixed plant[2]
- tree planting and general horticultural work
- positioning and removal of lightweight moveable partitions
- surveying[3]
- work to or on ships and mobile offshore installations
- off-site manufacture of items for later use in construction
- fabrication of elements for offshore installations
- on-site construction of fixed offshore oil and gas installations.

Whilst this distinction has not been carried into the current guidance document,[4] it still stands as a useful steer on work that could fall outside the requirements of the CDM Regulations 2015. However, often such work, particularly 'surveying', is simply an activity within the larger project and it is the project and its activities that must be viewed in the light of the compliance requirements of the CDM Regulations 2015. Thus, for the purpose of the CDM Regulations 2015, the question of whether work is solely 'surveying' or is 'surveying as an activity associated with the larger project' must be considered.

Note: The construction professional cannot cherry-pick early-stage activities and assume that they stand outside the compliance requirements of the project. Reference to the definitions on the previous page provides clarification that 'preparation for an intended structure, including site clearance, exploration, investigation, etc.' indicates that the project has started even if there is a time period between these activities finishing and the project proper starting.

A different standpoint could be taken if these early activities were independent and an end in themselves, with no intention of pursuing further construction work.

The pursuit of compatibility with the CDM Regulations 2015 must not obscure the legal need for compliance with other relevant construction-related legislation, with

---

[2]   As distinct from major component replacement activity.

[3]   As distinct from 'site investigation'.

[4]   *Managing health and safety in construction. Guidance on Regulations.* L153. HSE, ISBN 9780717666263, published 2015.

particular emphasis on the 'duty of care' implications enshrined in the Health and Safety at Work etc. Act 1974:

> General duties of employers to their employees.
> (1)
> It shall be the duty of every employer to ensure, so far as is reasonably practicable, the health, safety and welfare at work of all his employees

A similar duty applies towards non-employees affected by the employer's undertaking.

* * * * * * * * * * * * * * * * * *

Within the CDM Regulations, duties may be 'absolute', governed by the term *must*, and carrying an extremely onerous obligation, for example:

> Regulation 4
> A client must make suitable arrangements for managing a project.

Alternatively, duties may be governed by terms such as *so far as is reasonably practicable*, for example:

> Regulation 11(1)
> the principal designer must … plan, manage and monitor the pre-construction phase …
> so far as is reasonably practicable.

The term 'so far as is reasonably practicable' allows professional judgment to be exercised, however, when used together with the absolute term 'must', it establishes a more complex arrangement of words. Legal advice on its interpretation advises that a qualified duty supported by strict liability cannot be defined as absolute.

* * * * * * * * * * * * * * * * * * * *

The term 'project manager' does not appear in the Regulations, indicative of the fact that the Regulations do not fully mirror the language of the construction industry. Thus, the language of the construction industry has to be overlaid with the language of construction law, the latter carrying the greater weight. Since the term project manager is not identified in the Regulations, efforts have to be made to consider the duties performed by the project manager, since, as a senior management role, it inevitably carries dutyholder responsibilities. However, the fact that the term is not absolutely defined and that project manager is a position carrying differing responsibilities in different organisations could lead to different levels of obligation, dependent on organisational definition.

The task is easier with terms such as sub-contractor, sub-designer, permanent designer and temporary works designer, for the dutyholder clue lies in the name, but a further challenge exists when consideration is given to the terms agent, works manager and temporary works coordinator. The CDM dutyholder needs an understanding of the industry and the range of management models associated with different procurement routes, since they may lead to numerous and varied statutory arrangements.

3 Application

These Regulations apply to all construction work,[1] undertaken in Great Britain, as defined by Regulation 3: Application:

1. These Regulations apply—

    (a) in Great Britain; and

    (b) to premises and activities outside Great Britain to which sections 1 to 59 and 80 to 82 of the 1974 Act apply by virtue of articles 9 and 11(1)(a) of the Health and Safety at Work etc. Act 1974 (Application outside Great Britain) Order 2013.[2]

The structure of the Regulations divides the Statutory Instrument into the following sections:

Parts	
1	Regulation 1: Citation and commencement; Regulation 2: Interpretation; Regulation 3: Application in and outside Great Britain
2	Client duties: Regulation 4 to Regulation 7
3	Health and safety duties and roles: Regulation 8 to Regulation 15
4	General requirements for all construction sites: Regulation 16 to Regulation 35
5	Regulation 36: Enforcement in respect of fire; Regulation 37: Transitional and saving provisions; Regulation 38: Revocation and consequential amendments; Regulation 39: Review
Schedules	
1	Notification details
2	Minimum welfare arrangements
3	Work involving particular risks
4	Transitional and saving provisions
5	Amendments

(Continued)

---

[1] Refer definitions in Regulation 3.

[2] The Health and Safety at Work etc. Act 1974 (Application outside Great Britain) Order 2013 v6 came into force on the 6 April 2013 and applies particularly to offshore installations and associated work within the territorial sea or a renewable energy zone. It re-enacts the previous provisions of the H&SWAct1974 and introduces new articles associated with emerging energy technologies.

CDM Regulations 2015 Procedures Manual, Fourth Edition. Stuart D. Summerhayes.
© 2016 John Wiley & Sons, Ltd. Published 2016 by John Wiley & Sons, Ltd.

APPENDICES	
1	The general principles of prevention
2	Pre-construction information
3	The construction phase plan
4	The health and safety file
5	Summary of construction project information relationships
6	Working for a domestic client

The language above makes reference to Great Britain, to the exclusion of the Channel Islands,[3] the Isle of Man[4] and Northern Ireland,[5] who have not yet invoked the legislation through their own parliamentary processes. However, all excluded parties work closely to secure the intent of the CDM Regulations 2015.

Hence, these Regulations apply to any construction project undertaken in Great Britain and under the Health and Safety at Work etc. Act 1974 (Application outside Great Britain) Order 2013. They also apply to construction work carried out:

(a)   in its territorial waters[6]

(b)   in connection with, or preparatory to, construction of any renewable energy structure in the renewable energy zone.[7]

Note: The Regulations apply regardless of where the client resides or where the other dutyholder parties are based. Furthermore they apply regardless of construction project duration, financial cost or notification, and are guided response-wise by the words *proportionate* and *appropriate*.

Additional duties may exist for a client or anyone involved in the project who appoints designers based outside Great Britain.[8]

The colour-coordinated tabulation Figure 3.1 identifies Regulations and corresponding dutyholder responsibilities.

---

[3]   The CDM Regulations do not apply in the Channel Islands as they are not part of Britain and they have their own powers to make laws. The islands are not part of the European Union (EU) so will not be expected to follow the EU's Temporary or Mobile Construction Sites Directive.

[4]   The Regulations do not apply on the Isle of Man. While it is part of the United Kingdom, it has its own parliament and government, which have competence over all domestic matters. The island is not part of the EU, so is not expected to follow the EU's Temporary or Mobile Construction Sites Directive.

[5]   Northern Ireland has similar legislation known as Construction (Design and Management) Regulations (Northern Ireland) 2007, which is based on the European Union's Temporary or Mobile Construction Sites Directive. The consultation process leading to the update of these Regulations closed on 23 March 2015, with the new CDM Regulations now expected late 2016.

[6]   Territorial waters or territorial sea is defined by the 1982 United Nations Convention on the Law of the Sea as a belt of coastal waters extending at most 12 nautical miles (22.2 km; 13.8 miles) from the mean low-water mark of a coastal state.

[7]   The Renewable Energy Zone was declared under section 84 of the Energy Act 2004. It extends up to a maximum of 200 nautical miles from the mean low-water mark of a coastal state. The UK has claimed exclusive rights within this zone with respect to the production of energy from water or wind.

[8]   Refer Regulation 10.

APPLICABLE DUTYHOLDER REGULATIONS

	PART 1			PART 2				PART 3							PART 4		SCHEDULES & APPENDICES	PART 5 (not included)
	1 CITATION	2 INTERPRETATION	3 APPLICATION	4	5	6	7	8	9	10	11	12	13	14	15	16 to 35	SCHEDULES (1 to 5) / APPENDICES (1 to 6)	
CLIENT (commercial)																		
CLIENT (domestic)					not 5(3) or 5(4)													
DESIGNER																		
PRINCIPAL DESIGNER (PD)																		
CONTRACTOR																		
PRINCIPAL CONTRACTOR (PC)																		

PRE-CONSTRUCTION INFORMATION Appendix 2
- Client has the main duty to provide such information to designers (incl. PD) and contractors (incl. PC). For single contractor projects it is the Client's duty alone.
- Close liaison between Client and PD in progressing this document and associated process.
- Contractor and Principal Contractor have no specific duties in respect of Pre-construction Information.

CONSTRUCTION PHASE PLAN (CP Plan) Appendix 3
- For single contractor projects the contractor has the responsibility for ensuring a CP Plan is drawn up.
- Lead taken by PC in preparation, reviewing, updating and revising of this document *where there is more than one contractor*.
- Designer has no specific duty in respect of the drafting of the CP Plan, but must provide relevant information.

HEALTH AND SAFETY FILE (H & S File) Appendix 4
- **ONLY REQUIRED FOR PROJECTS INVOLVING MORE THAN ONE CONTRACTOR.**
- Client to ensure the PD prepares the H & S File and that it is updated, reviewed and revised throughout the project.
- H & S File passed to the Client by the PD once project is finished, or if PD has left the project then the duty falls to PC.
- Further legal duties remain with the Client after its receipt.

Regulations: 4: Client duties; 5: Appointment of PD and PC; 6: Notification; 7: Domestic Clients; 8: General duties; 9: Designers; 10: Outside GB; 11: Duties of PD at pre-construction phase; 12: Construction phase plan and Health & Safety File; 13: Duties of PC at construction phase; 14: PC duties to consult/engage with workers; 15: Duties of contractors; 16 to 35: General requirements for all construction sites.

Figure 3.1 Dutyholder responsibilities.

4 Dutyholders

4.1 Introduction

The holistic diagram below, Figure 4.1, is an illustrative representation of the dutyholder functions together with the associated processes and the overlapping boundaries of project stages.

It is more realistic to visualise the project stage boundaries as elastic, for they can vary with procurement strategies.

A working familiarity with the detail of these Regulations is vital for the construction professional, not only in respect of his/her own role, but in the appreciation of the duties to be discharged by other dutyholders within the team. Dutyholder interaction is essential for the successful delivery of health and safety management within the project, dependent upon effective communication and cooperation throughout all project phases.

On all construction projects[1] there will be a client, designer and contractor, formally or informally appointed, with duties to discharge under the CDM Regulations 2015. These positions all carry statutory duties, regardless of project duration or project cost. Where there is more than one contractor on the project at any one time, the client must appoint a principal contractor and a principal designer in writing. These latter two appointments[2] are the only statutory appointments that the client has to make under the CDM Regulations 2015, since all other appointments are contractual, although carrying statutory duties.

The same organisation could perform all the dutyholder roles provided it can demonstrate the necessary skills, experience, training and organisational capability, and undertakes such duties from commitment and not convenience.

4.1.1 Dutyholders

In accordance with the superscript numbering in Figure 4.1, the following narrative provides some further insights:

1 CLIENT: Number one in the supply chain and able to exert great influence over the project, albeit with guidance from his professional advisory team. It is his support, particularly to the principal designer, and his understanding of the role of the principal contractor, which are key areas for project success.

---

[1] As defined by Regulation 2.

[2] Such appointments are NOT linked to the notification process – Regulation 6.

CDM Regulations 2015 Procedures Manual, Fourth Edition. Stuart D. Summerhayes.
© 2016 John Wiley & Sons, Ltd. Published 2016 by John Wiley & Sons, Ltd.

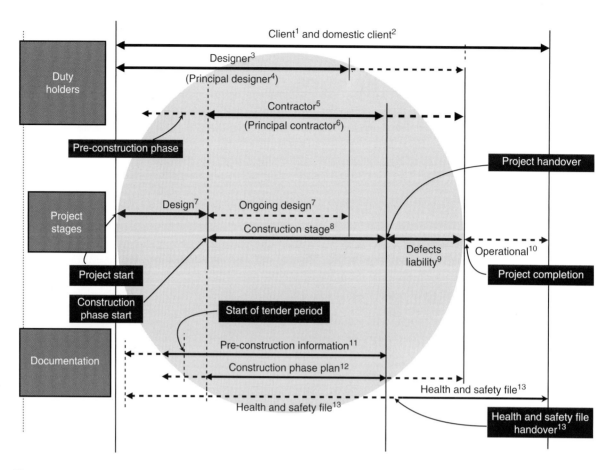

Figure 4.1 Holistic diagram.

The client as dutyholder is the only party whose skills, knowledge, experience and operational capability is not assessed, but all designers and contractors have a duty to ensure that the client is aware of his duties. It should not end there, for such dutyholders should thereafter ensure that the client is discharging his duties, by his performance or otherwise, and if he is not, they must take appropriate action as early as possible.

It is the client who is the author of 'pre-construction information' on a single contractor project and who will be the initiator of such information on every project until the appointment of the principal designer.

The law further distinguishes between 'lay clients' and 'informed clients'. The former are representative of those clients, new to construction, who have only ever had a limited exposure to the construction industry. The latter are those clients with a building portfolio who are regularly involved in extensions and new builds as part of business expansion and/or alteration. It is obvious that the 'lay client' needs more support, but the duties placed on both types of client are exactly the same.

2 DOMESTIC CLIENT: Client duties apply to all domestic client projects, but all responsibilities on the domestic client[3] are undertaken by the contractor, principal contractor, designer or principal designer (by prior agreement), with no default transfer of duties back to the domestic client himself.

---

[3] The distinction between the domestic property being built by a developer and that being directly built for the owner rests on whether this work is done in the course or furtherance of a business. If it is the former then the full ramifications of these Regulations apply; if the latter then Regulation 7 applies.

The appointment of a principal designer and principal contractor is an option that can be exercised by the domestic client, but if not exercised, then by default the designer becomes the principal designer and the contractor in control of the construction phase becomes the principal contractor.[4]

The duties of designer and contractor must always be fulfilled by those parties undertaking domestic project design-related or construction-related activities.

3 DESIGNER: identified as number two in the supply chain and usually operating as the professional advisor to the client. Historically there are strong links between clients and designers, who have for many years operated together and forged mutually beneficial business arrangements. On a larger project there could be a number of multi-disciplinary design teams, with a greater requirement for design coordination.

Other than on the smallest of projects, design itself is rarely complete and continues to develop incrementally over a period of time, possibly well into the construction phase, dependent on procurement strategy. The design management process must offer flexibility for change, within feasible limits, to accommodate later alterations and variations, hopefully with the knowledge that late change incurs greater cost, with additional implications for those down the supply chain working within the confines of a construction programme.

4 PRINCIPAL DESIGNER: this is an appointment that must now be made by the client in writing on all projects where it is foreseeable that there will be more than one contractor on site at any one time. It is therefore an appointment made on the basis of future foreseeability, and preferably one made as early in the design process as is practicable.

This is a key role, whose purpose is to control the pre-construction phase of the project from concept design, through the planning stages and up to the delivery of the construction work. This is achieved through planning, managing, monitoring and coordinating health and safety matters relevant to the project at this stage.

It is the principal designer, once appointed, who becomes the author of the 'pre-construction information' (refer superscript item 11) on a project where there will be more than one contractor, and who is also the dutyholder charged with the collation and drafting of the health and safety file up to the end of the period of his design commission.

Early and constant dialogue is required between the principal designer and the principal contractor throughout the pre-construction and construction phases.[5]

5 CONTRACTOR: the party executing the project during the construction phase either solely or in conjunction with other contractors. The definition of contractor[6] ensures that the sole operator and the larger contractor with a reservoir of directly employed operatives are both defined as a single contractor under the CDM Regulations 2015. This has implications for determining how many contractors are likely to be on site at any one time, as this is a critical condition and a trigger for the appointment of both the principal designer and the principal contractor.

Commonsense must prevail and the management control model for the large contractor with his own domestic workforce should replicate that of the principal contractor on a similar sized multi-contractor project in terms of the management infrastructure of roles and responsibilities.

---

[4]   Regulation 7(2).

[5]   Regulations 11(7) and 13(5).

[6]   Regulation 2.

4 Dutyholders

A management control perspective focused on the achievement of *safe* and *suitable* conditions would need on occasion to do more than simply comply, and a 'best practice' approach is to be recommended.

The author of the statutory 'construction phase plan' (refer superscript item 12) is either the single contractor or alternately the principal contractor, depending on project arrangements. All projects must now sufficiently prepare such a document prior to the start of construction and further develop it throughout the construction phase compatible with the changing programme of works.

6 PRINCIPAL CONTRACTOR: as with the principal designer, such an appointment must be made by the client in writing on all projects where it is foreseeable that there will be more than one contractor on site at any one time.

This dutyholder is responsible for managing the construction stage, and all activities undertaken within the curtilage of his construction site come under his jurisdiction. The client has no legal right to interfere in the principal contractor's management of this process and therefore, once the principal contractor has been appointed, the client becomes subordinate to the principal contractor's management role in matters of construction phase management, other than for emergency strategic management, when construction work is being undertaken within a more hazardous operational working environment.

It is not necessary that the principal contractor supervises all the activities of the specialist sub-contractors on site but he must remain satisfied that their individual management systems are satisfactory and remain effective throughout.

Where construction projects are undertaken within an operational site under the control of the client there must be clearly demarcated areas of control for both client and principal contractor. The principal contractor will retain control over the construction site and the client over the remaining operational site, but coordination and communication must establish who has the overriding duty in emergency situations. The outcome should be unambiguous and dependent upon the ownership of the hazards associated with the emergency.

The principal contractor is the author of the 'construction phase plan' (refer superscript item 12) and must suitably develop it throughout the construction phase.

4.1.2 Project stages

7 DESIGN: Regardless of the procurement strategy, design is rarely if ever complete before construction begins. Even on the conventional project such as a 'Bill of Quantities' contract, design change and alteration will affect and extend the design process.

More projects are now undertaken under the 'design and build' option, with specialised work packages being let later into the process. These inevitably have a design input, often towards the latter stages of construction, and thus design can continue right up to the end of the construction stage itself.

Design of the permanent asset, referred to as 'permanent design' is distinct from 'temporary works design', undertaken by the contractor in order to deliver the permanent design solution. Both come under the definition of design and therefore both sets of designers are subject to the same duties under the CDM Regulations 2015. It should also be noted that there are cases, particularly at the cusp of technical innovation, where the temporary works design is the more innovative and can represent the larger financial investment.

Hence, temporary works design cannot escape the attention of the client[7] or principal designer,[8] and should not be overlooked, for it is an equally essential part of design risk management, subject to the same regulations.

Obligations under the Regulations are dependent only on the potential design use in construction work in Great Britain and hence design duties exist regardless of the presence of a client, and as outlined in paragraph 77/L153 include work on concept design, competitions, bids for grants, modifications of existing designs and relevant work undertaken as feasibility studies.

8 CONSTRUCTION STAGE: The construction phase start is critical and construction projects that start without adequate preparation and planning can rarely if ever be delivered successfully. It also represents the 'sharp end' of construction, for the construction phase environment is simultaneously hostile, dynamic and rapidly changing.

Complacency must be avoided throughout and health and safety control processes must be continually reviewed, revised and refined to ensure they deliver a *safe* and *suitable* environment for all who may be affected by the processes. It is this exercise that provides the rigour and robustness to ensure that management control systems continue to deliver and protect.

At the end of the construction stage, which can be extended via the granting of agreed 'extensions of time', the completed project is handed over and accepted by the client subject to all the outstanding items on the 'snagging list' being duly completed. The Health and Safety File' (refer superscript item 13) should then be received by the client from either the principal designer or principal contractor, dependent on commissioning arrangements.[9]

9 DEFECTS LIABILITY PERIOD: also referred to as the *maintenance period* and extending usually to six or twelve months after project handover. This period places contractual responsibility on the principal contractor/contractor to remedy defective workmanship that becomes evident in this period, through quality issues or inferior workmanship.

If such work arises from a defective design statement, then it must be completed nonetheless, but at the client's cost, possibly counter-charged to the responsible design team, where appropriate.

Such work remains subject to the CDM Regulations 2015 and related construction legislation, even though earlier control arrangements will have lapsed through changes associated with ownership, environment, operations and contractual disconnections.

The start of the defects liability period also marks the changeover of insurance responsibility from the principal contractor/contractor to the client. It is therefore a key moment in project ownership as reflected by the release of half of the retention money.[10]

10 OPERATIONAL STAGE: At this stage all payments should have been made to the contracting team, and the client and his management team now have operating and managerial responsibilities for the asset.

---

[7] Regulation 4(1) and 4(3).

[8] Regulation 11(4) and 11(7).

[9] Regulation 12(8) and 12(10).

[10] Depending on contractual arrangements, retention money is deducted each month from the monthly payment made to the contractor for work done to date. It is retained to cover the correction of defective workmanship and materials. Half of this retention money is released to the principal contractor/contractor at project handover, i.e. the start of the defects liability period, and the remaining half at the end of this period. Smaller jobs often take a more informal approach.

4 Dutyholders

The operational time period varies with design codes, but more valuable assets should be supported by asset management plans and life-cycle strategic planning.

These considerations could well have an impact on the format and content of health and safety files, since reliability analysis will dictate the period between major component replacements. Key service decisions will affect the guidance provided in respect of the rigour and frequency of testing, and the corresponding narrative should be captured and catalogued in the health and safety files.

The longevity of every asset is dependent on inspection and maintenance, the extent of which reflects the sensitivity of the asset to its environmental surroundings, working conditions and the health and safety consequences of component failure. Consideration of these issues over the asset's lifespan is a feature of the design process, one which represents an obligation on design teams to provide relevant information and guidance in the health and safety file accounting for lifespan implications during the operational phase.

It should also be noted that day-to-day maintenance is not subject to the CDM Regulations, unlike major component replacement information. This should also provide a focus for the authors of health and safety files, who would need to have a perspective on replacement cycles and outage periods.[11]

4.1.3 Documentation

More and more paperwork does not help to deliver safer and more suitable health and safety working arrangements. Managerial attention needs to be constantly focused on delivering succinct, project-specific information based on *significant* issues relevant to the project.

The spectre of past criticism directed at excessive bureaucracy must be countered before it again haunts the document management process. This requires managers to exercise judgment in the communication of essential information. Dutyholder teams should be competent and must have the characteristics associated with the requirements of Regulations 8 and 15(7).[12] Therefore there is no need for any dutyholder to peddle obvious statements relating to issues that by experience and expectation would be managed on all such projects.

This remains a clarion call to all document authors, who need to exercise judgment in delivering such information as the key narrative of document content. In many ways, the value of the document content lies in the irrelevance omitted as well as the quality of the information the document contains, which must be promptly provided in a comprehensible form.

Since all construction projects must deliver pre-construction information and a construction phase plan, a perspective on *appropriateness* and *proportionality* must accompany the collation and editing of content, based on a commonsense approach, in order to reduce irrelevance and to deliver focused information.

The documents described below are delivered as a result of process management and are not time-barred, for all documents arise as part of a process that requires them to be updated and their currency maintained during their respective lifetimes. Thus, there is no final document as such, for they all represent a state of transition, with further additions and updates possible throughout the ensuing dynamic process,

---

[11] Downtime or outage duration refers to a period of time when a system fails to provide or perform its primary function.

[12] Both Regulations require designers and contractors to have 'the skills, knowledge and experience and, if they are an organisation, the organisational capability, necessary to fulfil the role'.

with inputs required pre-construction, during construction and long after handover in the case of the health and safety file.

11 PRE-CONSTRUCTION INFORMATION: this must be provided to all contractors and designers who might be appointed, for every construction project. Its author is initially the client, who must make reasonable enquiries to provide relevant information. This client process is assisted by the principal designer when appointed, and is therefore greatly facilitated by the principal designer's judicious appointment at the earliest opportunity.

The pre-construction information is dependent on the retrieval of historical and current information, which may or may not be available. This potential lack of availability, through mismanagement, loss or indifference, could well cost the client a further upfront expense. Consequently, one of the first actions to be taken by the principal designer once appointed is to establish the status quo of relevant information and advise the client of missing items. No party is allowed to take an all-risk approach to the management of health and safety.

Pre-construction information is required before the construction activity itself takes place and is not related solely to the period before the construction phase starts. As with all such information it should be provided promptly and in a suitable format (see section 6.2).

12 CONSTRUCTION PHASE PLAN: this is possibly the most important of all documents since it articulates the health and safety management control arrangements for all work activities during the construction phase. Its author is either the sole contractor on a single contractor site or the principal contractor on the multiple-contractor site.

The title of this document, unfortunately, connects the 2007 version of the Regulations, which required it only on notifiable projects. It was therefore associated with the larger project and hence has connotations of greater formality and detailed content. Previous experiences must not be allowed to jaundice the wider role and purpose now fulfilled by such a document. Hence, different versions covering the full spectrum of project complexities can be anticipated.

Since it is required on all construction projects, many single contractors will now have to provide such a legal document. It is obvious that such a document must be delivered in a suitable format for both the small construction work as well as the mega-project under the auspices of the multi-disciplinary project team. Commonsense and prudence will need to be exercised to ensure that the response is appropriate to the health and safety issues that need to be managed and the wider context that will, for the foreseeable future, be covered by a similarly named document.

The construction phase plan is a control document providing detail of a dynamic situation, whose usefulness depends on the ability of the control process to ensure the review, updating and revision of those controls in representation of the changing site situation. It embraces inputs from site management and operatives in a two-way arrangement so that the predictive controls outlined by management can quickly respond to feedback about the effectiveness of those controls or otherwise as the work activity unfolds. Prompt exchange is as critical between the various construction teams and the principal contractor as it is between the directly employed operative and the single contractor.

Inevitably, it must also respond to design change, which provides further challenges during construction since operational amendment must now be accommodated within the confines of the construction programme. Close interface communication is as essential between the principal contractor and principal designer as it is between the contractor and designer.

13 HEALTH AND SAFETY FILE: this is a reference document for the client in respect of future alterations/amendments/modifications to the asset as handed over to the client. Its initial collator is the principal designer. Note that there would not be a health and safety file on a single contractor project.

However, it is wise to separate out the 'duty of care' requirement to provide relevant information under all circumstances[13] and the need to provide information for the health and safety file under specific circumstances.

Regulation 12(5) infers that a health and safety file must always be prepared by the principal designer. There will be projects with a principal designer which by their very nature will have no content to deliver into a health and safety file. It is important that the health and safety file management process demonstrates the steps by which the decision that there is no relevant content arose, rather than that there be no visibility regarding the health and safety file.

Regulation 12(10) directs that the health and safety file be handed to the client at 'the end of the project'. This point in time is not defined and could be represented by the end of the construction phase[14] or the end of defects liability period or somewhere in between. This handover point for the health and safety file should be identified before the start of the project, reflecting the critical operational necessity of such information taking into account project complexity. Account must also be taken of the partially complete health and safety file that should accompany partial handover or sectional completion etc.

Table 4.1 illustrates the dutyholder arrangements and the interrelationship of duties, colour-coordinated as per Figure 3.1. Please note the distinction between the heavier and lighter cell boundaries, as outlined in notes 1 and 2 at the bottom of the Table.

4.2   Client

The Regulations acknowledge the critical role of the client in influencing the health and safety management outcomes of any project. This acknowledgement is based on the client's position as lead in the supply chain and his strategic ability to establish and promote the contractual climate that creates the successful project ambience. It is this influential position which ensures the continuing client role in:

- monitoring of the management arrangements of others (Regulations 4(1), 4(2), 4(3))

- the provision of key information (Regulations 4(4), 8(6))

- process control management (Regulation 4(5))

- the taking of reasonable steps to ensure the principal contractor and principal designer roles are being complied with (Regulation 4(6))

- management of the health and safety file (Regulation 4(7))

- the notification process (Regulation 7)

- the appointment process (Regulations 8(3), 10(1))

- cooperation with others (Regulation 8(4)).

---

[13] Regulations 8(6)(a), 9(4) and 15(9).
[14] This was the situation stated in Regulation 20(2)(f) of the 2007 Regulations.

Table 4.1 Dutyholder interfaces

Dutyholder interfaces

Is work construction by definition?

- YES → CDM Regns APPLY
- NO → CDM Regns DO NOT APPLY

Defined in Regulation 2 in respect of 'the construction of a structure'.

NOTE: For specific detail in respect of individual Regulations please refer to the appropriate section.

MAJOR CHANGE! APPOINTMENTS ARE NOT RELATED TO THE NOTIFICATION PROCESS.

Client must appoint a principal contractor and principal designer in writing if it is **foreseeable that more than one contractor will be working.**

(If one contractor) → Principal designer / Client
(If > one contractor) → Contractor / Principal contractor

Statutory appointments by client if it is foreseeable that more than one contractor is on site at any one time. — *Before construction phase begins.*

Both these appointments are contractual.

Reg	Title	Principal designer	Designer	Client	Contractor	Principal contractor	Commentary	Timings
4	Client duties in relation to managing projects.	H&S File; compliance with Regs 11&12.	Management arrangements.	Management arrangements; pre-construction information; construction phase plan; H&S File mgt; PD duties and PC duties.	Management arrangements.	CP Plan; compliance with Regs 12 to 14.	Management arrangements for all dutyholders to be effective.	Throughout the project.
5	Appointment of the principal designer and principal contractor.	Default duty through failure to appoint.		Appointments of principal designer and principal contractor.	Default duty through failure to appoint.		Failure by the client to appoint, in writing, at the appropriate time, ensures that both duties default to the client!!	Preferably ASAP but definitely pre-start of construction phase.
6	Notification.			Notification of project.	Dependent on site construction work lasting longer than 30 working days AND > 20 workers working simultaneously, or ...>500 person days.		Appointments are not related to notification!! principal designer can facilitate.	ASAP but before the construction phase begins.
7	Application to domestic clients.	Could function as client by agreement in writing.	If Reg 5 appointments are not made by the client then the designer in control of pre-construction is the principal designer.	(Domestic client)	Single contractor could function as client.	Client duties to be carried out by the principal contractor on multi-contractor site. If Reg 5 appointments are not made by the client then the contractor in control of construction is the principal contractor.	All domestic client duties fall to others with no default rebound onto the client.	Throughout the construction phase.
8	General duties.	Competence. Co-operation. Reporting. Information/instruction.	Competence. Cooperation. Reporting. Information/instruction.	Competence. Co-operation. Reporting. Information/instruction.	Competence. Co-operation. Reporting. Information/instruction.	Competence. Co-operation. Reporting. Information/instruction.	All appointees must have suitable skills, knowledge, experience and operational capability. Cooperation with others working at the same or adjoining construction sites.	Before appointment. Throughout the project period.

(Continued)

4 Dutyholders

Table 4.1 (Continued)

#	Duty	Refer pages: 43–51	Refer pages: 35–42	Refer pages: 24–35	Refer pages: 52–59	Refer pages: 54, 60–69	Notes	Timing
9	Duties of designers.	Client awareness. General principles of prevention. Provision of information.		In respect of any temporary works design.			NOTE: Designer duties fall to both permanent design and temporary works design.	At the start. Throughout the project.
10	Designs prepared or modified outside Great Britain.		Relevant dutyholder to ensure Regulation 9 duties are complied with.				Responsibility by the person who commissions the design if established in Great Britain, otherwise by the client.	Prior to overseas design appointment and throughout the project.
11	Duties of a principal designer in relation to health and safety at pre-construction phase.	Plan and manage. General principles of prevention. Regulation 9 designer duties. Cooperation. PC Information. Liaison with principal contractor	Regulation 9 designer duties. Cooperation. Receipt of pre-construction information	Cooperation.	Receipt of pre-construction information.	Receipt of pre-construction information. Liaison with the principal designer.	NOTE: initially pre-construction information would go out to tendering contractors, one of whom will become the principal contractor.	Pre-construction phase and throughout the project.
12	Construction phase plan and the health and safety file.	Information. H&S File management.				CP Plan management. Information management for H&S File.	Principal designer commission period could effect final management of H&S File. CHECK!! (Reg 12(8))	Pre-construction phase and throughout the project.
13	Duties of a principal contractor in relation to health and safety at the construction phase.	Liaison with principal contractor.		Cooperation/coordination. Follow CP Plan.		Manage effectively. General principles of prevention. Contractor cooperation/coordination. Site induction: site security: welfare Liaison with principal designer.		Pre-construction phase and throughout the construction phase.
14	Principal contractor's duties to consult and engage with workers					Manage contractor cooperation. Consult with workforce. Enable inspection of relevant information.		Throughout the construction phase.
15	Duties of contractors.	Refer above under 'Duties of designers'.		Client awareness. Management of work. Compliance with directions. General principles of prevention. CP Plan management.* Supervision; instruction & training. Site security and welfare.			NOTE: Design duties (temporary works) have also to be discharged by the majority of contractors.	Throughout the construction phase.
Part 4	General requirements for all construction sites.	Dependent on there being only one contractor on the site throughout the construction phase.					In other words domestic client, **NEVER** tell the contractor how to do it!!	Throughout the construction phase.

NOTE: 1	Refer pages: 43–51	Refer pages: 35–42	Refer pages: 24–35	Refer pages: 52–59	Refer pages: 54, 60–69
Cells with heavy boundaries are indicative of primary holder statutory duties.					

NOTE: 2	Refer pages: 43–51	Refer pages: 35–42	Refer pages: 24–35	Refer pages: 52–59	Refer pages: 54, 60–69
Cells with lighter boundaries are indicative of dutyholder response duties to the primary dutyholder.					

The visible and substantive involvement of the client is a key factor in the ability of the principal designer to effectively discharge his duties and is also a critical support interface with the contractor on the smaller project, where there is no requirement to appoint a principal contractor. As with all dutyholder roles it requires a proactive involvement, which for the client does not translate into taking an active role in managing the work. However, the client is required to exercise ownership and to ensure suitable arrangements for managing the project are made and maintained throughout the design and construction phases. This is a statutory vigilance and is a necessary contribution towards effective health and safety management delivery by the other dutyholders over the duration of the project. This invariably involves dependence on the client's professional team.

The use of consultancy support must remain a facilitative device, for the client has executive and contractual control over procurement strategy, key appointments, project logistics and process control, all of which impact directly or indirectly on the management of health and safety.

Under the Regulations the client must now appreciate the:

- separation of appointment and notification processes
- default mechanism in respect of failure to appoint
- change in the criteria for notification
- single and multiple contractor situation
- benefit of early principal designer appointment
- change in process controls associated with the start of construction
- necessity for pre-construction information and the construction phase plan
- due emphasis required to be placed on health and safety file management

and must acknowledge his exposure to criminal prosecution by the HSE (or ORR[15] or ONR[16]) should there be a failure to discharge statutory duties.

Hence, the CDM Regulations 2015 make the client accountable for the impact his/her decisions have on the health, safety and welfare outcomes of the construction project.

The client and his professional advisors should be aware of the necessary distinction between the baseline of compliance and the benchmark standard of 'best practice'. There are occasions when the latter provides the better objective yardstick, e.g.

Regulation	Detail	Commentary
Regulation 9(1)	'A designer must not commence work in relation to a project unless satisfied that the client is aware of the duties owed by the client under these Regulations.'	The designer–client interface should not be limited to a literal interpretation, for the client's subsequent understanding of his duties needs to be shadowed throughout the project and appropriate action taken if duties are not being discharged because of ignorance, complacency or lack of clarity.
Regulation 15(1)	Similarly for the contractor	ditto

[15] Office of Rail and Road Regulation. Refer Regulation 6(4).
[16] Office of Nuclear Regulation. Refer Regulation 6(5).

The client must make suitable arrangements for managing the project and establishing a methodology for ensuring that the management arrangements of other dutyholders remain effective throughout the project. Such arrangements could include the need to:

- focus on project content and complexity

- ensure roles, functions and responsibilities are clarified

- establish and monitor effective mechanisms for communication and cooperation and their support by suitable coordination

- consider performance indicators, which can be used to measure principal designer and principal contractor management effectiveness

- be satisfied that welfare facilities are suitable and effective and remain so thereafter

and there is an ongoing duty to ensure that:

- notification is made (where relevant)

- appropriate appointments are made at the right time

- those appointed have the skills, knowledge, training and experience, together with the relevant organisational capability

- reasonable enquiries are made to furnish relevant content/details for pre-construction information

- a construction phase plan is sufficiently prepared before the construction phase begins and continues to be developed compatible with the programme of works thereafter

- a health and safety file is prepared and managed by the principal designer and/or principal contractor for projects with more than one contractor.[17]

A client duty summary sheet is included in the Appendices.

Table 4.2: Client duties, provides the detailed narrative.

4.3 Domestic client

The domestic client is defined in Regulation 2 as

> a client for whom a project is being carried out which is not in the course of furtherance of a business of that client.

Client duties exist on all domestic client projects and such projects involve the full remit of the Regulations. However, on such projects Regulation 7 ensures that the client duties must be performed by either the contractor or principal contractor, or the principal designer, which represents a variation from the commercial client scenario.

Thus the domestic client duties are carried out by the contractor on a single contractor site and by the principal contractor on a multiple contractor site, or by the principal designer if there is a written agreement with the client. This latter arrangement offers continuity for those domestic clients who have initially approached a designer for outline/detailed drawings and professional guidance prior to planning permission

---

[17] **Note:** if the principal designer appointment finishes before the end of the project (dependent on procurement strategy), the client should ensure that the health and safety file is handed to the principal contractor for its continued development (Reg. 12(8)).

Table 4.2 Client duties

No.	Reg.	Client duties — Regulation	Client duties — Commentary	Stage
1	2(1)	Defines client: '"client" means any person for whom the project is carried out'		
	4	**Client duties in relation to managing projects**		
2	4(1)	A client must make suitable arrangements for managing a project, including the allocation of sufficient time and other resources.	This refers to the client's own infrastructure arrangements as well as the management arrangements of the other dutyholders: designer, contractor, principal designer and principal contractor.	Prior to appointment.
3	4(2)	Arrangements are suitable if they ensure that— (a) the construction work can be carried out so far as is reasonably practicable without risk to the health and safety of any person affected by the project; and (b) the facilities required by Schedule 2 are provided in respect of any person carrying out construction work.	These are the health and safety management arrangements of the project, which extend to consideration of operatives, management, invited and non-invited visitors, as well as the public. Schedule 2 covers the welfare arrangements of the contractor and/or principal contractor.	**Note:** suitable welfare arrangements are required to be in place from day one of the construction phase start.
4	4(3)	A client must ensure that these arrangements are maintained and reviewed throughout the project.	A project dynamic requiring procedures to be in place to confirm with due frequency that management arrangements remain effective.	Throughout the project. Site meeting agendas should be structured to capture salient information. (Refer Appendices.)
5	4(4)	A client must provide pre-construction information as soon as is practicable to every designer and contractor appointed, or being considered for appointment, to the project.	A requirement to provide relevant project-specific information based on reasonable enquiries having been made by the client. No party can take an all-risk approach to managing hazardous aspects of the project. If relevant information is not available then there will be a further cost factor in its provision. Guidance on pre-construction information is provided in Appendix 2 of document L153.	Before design development; prior to tender stage; before the relevant activity is undertaken; and at key information stages throughout. Pre-construction information can be provided well into the construction phase of the project.
6	4(5)	A client must ensure that— (a) before the construction phase begins, a construction phase plan is drawn up by the contractor if there is only one contractor, or by the principal contractor; and (b) the principal designer prepares a health and safety file for the project, which— (i) complies with the requirements of regulation 12(5); (ii) is revised from time to time as appropriate to incorporate any relevant new information; and (iii) is kept available for inspection by any person who may need it to comply with the relevant legal requirements.	(a) This should be read in the context of Regulations 12(1), 12(2), 12(4) and 15(5). Particularly resonant is Regulation 12(4) which refers to the construction phase plan being *sufficient* to ensure health and safety. It is this condition that should be met in each case. Since this is the primary site control document it has implications touching on the client's duty under Regulations 4(1) and 4(3). Similar implications exist for those who advise the client. (b) (ii) It is this Regulation which requires the client to maintain any health and safety file up to date.	Before the construction phase begins. **Note:** preparatory works for the project indicate that the construction phase has started. This includes site clearance and the erection of boundary fencing etc. Throughout the project.

(Continued)

Table 4.2 (Continued)

No.	Reg.	Client duties		Stage
		Regulation	Commentary	
7	4(6)	*A client must take reasonable steps to ensure that—* (a) *the principal designer complies with any other principal designer duties in Regulations 11 and 12; and* (b) *the principal contractor complies with any other principal contractor duties in Regulations 12 and 14.*	The client must be able to demonstrate a system that supports the reasonable steps taken. This should not lead to an excessive bureaucratic response and can be achieved by the fine-tuning of agenda items with the capture of minuted responses to the valid agenda items. Guidance would usually be provided by the professional design team.	Throughout the project.
8	4(7)	*If a client disposes of the client's interest in the structure, the client complies with the duty in paragraph (5)(b)(iii) by providing the health and safety file to the person who acquires the client's interest in the structure and ensuring that that person is aware of the nature and purpose of the file.*	Thus the health and safety file becomes a vending condition of change of asset ownership. Note the client's ongoing duty to maintain the currency of all of his health and safety files.	At the point of asset transfer.
9	4(8)	*Where there is more than one client in relation to a project—* (a) *one or more of the clients may agree in writing to be treated for the purposes of these Regulations as the only client or clients; and* (b) *except for the duties specified in sub-paragraph (c) only the client or clients agreed in paragraph (a) are subject to the duties owed by a client under these Regulations;* (c) *the duties in the following provisions are owed by all clients* (i) *Regulation 8(4); and* (ii) *paragraph (4) and Regulation 8(6) to the extent that those duties relate to information in the possession of the client.*	This offers an improved ownership and communication option on the multi-client site, by client election in writing. Note that certain duties cannot be passed over in this way and include: • duty to co-operate • provision of pre-construction information • provision of prompt comprehensible information/instruction.	As soon as possible in the multi-contract relationship. Throughout the project.

5	Appointment of the principal designer and principal contractor		
10	5(1)	Where there is more than one contractor, or if it is reasonably foreseeable that more than one contractor will be working on a project at any time, the client must appoint in writing— (a) a designer with control over the pre-construction phase as principal designer; and (b) a contractor as principal contractor.	This foreseeability must be examined at the earliest opportunity for it enables the appointments of principal designer and principal contractor to be made at the opportune time for them to fulfil their function and discharge their duties. The wording is such that both appointments depend on the foreseeability of there being more than one contractor on site at any time. Therefore the principal designer role could be undertaken by the only designer on the project. These are the two statutory appointments that must be made by the client. No other dutyholder can make them.	Before the construction phase starts. Ideally the principal designer appointment should be made during the concept stage of the project and there is much merit in the principal contractor being appointed as early as possible in the design stage to facilitate early design/construction dialogue. Such an exchange benefits all projects.
11	5(2)	The appointments must be made as soon as practicable, and in any event, before the construction phase begins.	The earlier the principal designer appointment can be made the greater the opportunity of safeguarding the client's interests in the project.	As soon as practicable, but before the start of the construction phase.
12	5(3)	If the client fails to appoint a principal designer, the client must fulfil the duties of the principal designer in Regulations 11 and 12.	Failure to appropriately appoint either of these dutyholders ensures that the client by default will be deemed to be fulfilling the role.	As soon as practicable but before the start of the construction phase.
13	5(4)	If the client fails to appoint a principal contractor, the client must fulfil the duties of the principal contractor in Regulations 12 and 14.	Vigilance by the client's advisory team is essential to ensure that this eventuality does not occur inadvertently.	As soon as practicable but before the start of the construction phase.
6	Notification		
			One of the two documents that the HSE inspector would want to see on a notifiable site, the other being the construction phase plan… on all sites.	
14	6(1)	A project is notifiable if the construction work on a construction site is scheduled to— (a) last longer than 30 working days and have more than 20 workers working simultaneously at any point in the project ; or (b) exceed 500 person days.	As a result of the two conditions that now have to be met under Regulation 6(1)(a), there will be fewer notifiable projects. It is foreseeable that more projects will be triggered by the 500 person-day rule than previously.	As soon as practicable but before the construction phase begins. Note: the appointment process (Reg. 5) and the notification process (Reg. 6) are now UNRELATED.
15	6(2)	Where a project is notifiable, the client must give notice in writing to the Executive as soon as practicable before the construction phase begins.	The client has responsibility for notification, even though others (principal designer) can facilitate his notification.	As soon as practicable but before the construction phase begins.

(Continued)

4 Dutyholders

Table 4.2 (Continued)

No.	Reg.	Regulation	Client duties	
			Commentary	Stage
16	6(3)	*The notice must—* *(a) contain the particulars specified in Schedule 1* *(b) be clearly displayed in the construction site office in a comprehensible form where it can be read by any worker engaged in the construction work; and* *(c) if necessary, be periodically updated.*	Schedule 1 carries the legal content of notification, which is the basis of the F10 form. Preferentially submitted in electronic format. Specifically the notification is to be displayed in the construction site office and in a comprehensible form. This latter point is in keeping with HSE guidance on general information elsewhere and thus a language additional to English may have to be used to convey understanding.	Displayed throughout the construction phase in the site office. An amendment to be issued if significant information changes. Copies can be obtained via https://www.hse.gov.uk/forms/notification/f10.htm
17	6(4)	*Where a project includes construction work of a description for which the Office of Rail Regulation is the enforcing authority by virtue of Regulation 3 of the Health and Safety (Enforcing Authority for Railways and other Guided Transport Systems) Regulations 2006, the client must give notice to the Office of Rail Regulation instead of the Executive.*	Since 1 April 2015, this office has been re-launched as the Office for Rail and Road Regulation. The Office of Rail and Road is the independent safety and economic regulator for Britain's railways and is responsible for monitoring Highways England's management of the strategic road network – the motorways and main 'A' roads in England.	As soon as practicable but before the construction phase begins.
18	6(5)	*Where a project includes construction work on premises which are or are on—* *(a) a GB nuclear site (within the meaning given in Section 68 of the Energy Act 2013); or* *(b) an authorised defence site (within the meaning given in Regulation 2(1) of the Health and Safety (Enforcing Authority) Regulations 1998);* *(c) a new nuclear build site (within the meaning in Regulation 2A of those Regulations), the client must give notice to the Office for Nuclear Regulation instead of the Executive.*	This is a new inclusion not covered in the two previous versions of these Regulations and reflects the increase in de-commissioning works associated with ageing power stations and the start of new build that will shortly be delivered as part of the strategic delivery for electrical supplies.	As soon as practicable but before the construction phase begins.

7 Application to domestic clients

19	7(1)	Where the client is a domestic client the duties in Regulations 4(1) to (7) and 6 must be carried out by— (a) the contractor for a project where there is only one contractor; (b) the principal contractor for a project where there is more than one contractor; or (c) the principal designer where there is a written agreement that the principal designer will fulfil those duties.	The domestic client situation, like the commercial client situation, must comply with relevant CDM Regulations 2015. However, the client duties must be undertaken by the contractor, principal contractor or principal designer if sanctioned by agreement in writing between the client and principal designer.	Before project commencement and throughout.
20	7(2)	If a domestic client fails to make the appointments required by Regulation 5— (a) the designer in control of the pre-construction phase of the project is the principal designer (b) the contractor in control of the construction phase of the project is the principal contractor.	In contrast to the commercial client, failure to appoint either the principal designer or principal contractor would not incur any default arrangement on the client. The default mode would ensure the designer in control of pre-construction phase or the contractor in control of the construction phase fulfils the principal designer and principal contractor's roles respectively.	As soon as is practicable but definitely prior to the start of the construction phase.
21	7(3)	Regulation 5(3) and (4) does not apply to a domestic client.		

8 General duties

22	8(3)	A person who is responsible for appointing a designer or contractor to carry out work on a project must take reasonable steps to satisfy themselves that the designer or contractor fulfils the conditions in paragraph (1).	This applies to all parties who are making appointments, all of whom must ensure that the dutyholders they appoint 'have the skills, knowledge and experience and, if they are an organisation, the organisational capability, necessary to fulfil the role that they are appointed to undertake, in a manner that secures the health and safety of any person affected by the project' as covered by Regulation 8(1).	Prior to appointment and preferably prior to the invite to tender. **Note:** numerous parties are able to appoint both designers and contractors dependent on project procurement strategy. All appointing parties must comply at the requisite stage throughout.
23	8(4)	A person with a duty or function under these Regulations must cooperate with any other person working on or in relation to a project at the same or an adjoining construction site to the extent necessary to enable any person with a duty or function to fulfil that duty or function.	Although the cooperative direction is towards those at the same or adjoining construction sites, the perspective needs to focus on the external environment because work other than on the construction site itself could compromise/be compromised by someone else's management arrangements. Note the greater duty of care arising out of acts or omissions.	Throughout the project. A changing situation that has to be revisited with appropriate regularity to identify all cooperating parties.

(Continued)

Table 4.2 (Continued)

No.	Reg.	Regulation	Client duties	
			Commentary	**Stage**
24	8(6)	*Any person who is required by these Regulations to provide information or instruction must ensure the information or instruction is comprehensible and provided as soon as practicable.*	The prompt supply of information/instruction is a critical prerequisite of communication. Account must be taken of the requirement that such information should be provided in a form that can be understood by all relevant parties, all of whom must be managed effectively.	Prior to the need for such information and throughout the project. Such a need must be established well in advance. **Note:** the distinction between the dutyholder obligation to provide information generally and the dutyholder duty to provide specific information. Refer Reg. 9(4).
25	8(7)	*To the extent that they are applicable to a domestic client, the duties in paragraphs (3), (4) and (6) must be carried out by the person specified in Regulation 7(1).*	These are client duties which for the domestic client would be undertaken by either one of the following: the contractor, principal contractor or principal designer.	Prior to appointment and throughout the project.
10		**Designs prepared or modified outside Great Britain**		
26	10(1)	*Where a design is prepared or modified outside Great Britain for use in construction work to which these Regulations apply—* *(a) the person who commissions it, if established within Great Britain; or* *(b) if that person is not so established, the client for the project, must ensure that Regulation 9 is complied with.*	This could have implications for the client if the commissioning party appointing designers is itself not established within Great Britain. The client needs to ensure that such designers understand and execute design to the requirements of Regulation 9.	Situation needs to be established in advance of such appointments, which could occur at numerous points dependent on procurement strategy. Documentary evidence would need to be evident in the discharge of this duty. Focused workshops can offer assurances.
27	10(2)	***This Regulation does not apply to a domestic client.***	Domestic clients carry no such responsibilities.	

Note:

1. Client needs to establish early dialogue with the principal designer to determine the form and format of the health and safety file.
2. For consideration of criteria for the assessment of management arrangements refer to Appendices.
3. Where relevant and within the client's occupied premises, consideration must be given to any compromise effect on existing management arrangements as a result of the proposed construction project. Due action might need to be taken.

being obtained. This situation ensures that the client for the principal contractor is indeed the principal designer.

As with all other construction projects, design and contractor duties exist for all those fulfilling such project roles.

In contrast to the commercial client situation, failure by the domestic client to appoint a principal contractor and principal designer does not involve default duties falling onto the client as per Regulation 5(3) and 5(4). In such a case, by default the designer in control of the pre-construction phase is the principal designer and the contractor in control of the construction phase is the principal contractor.[18]

Care must be exercised in the definition of the domestic client project since, subject to the earlier definition of the domestic client, any work on a property to be sold on for gain ensures that such a client is not domestic but would be classified as a developer (commercial client) and therefore not subject to the specifics of Regulation 7. Such a perspective similarly applies for work in connection with a business attached to a property.

Attention is also drawn to Part 4, Regulation 16(3):

> A domestic client who controls the way in which any construction work is carried out by a person at work must comply with the requirements of this Part so far as they relate to matters within the client's control.

This statement, from Part 4 of the Regulations: 'General requirements for all construction sites', should remind domestic clients not to control such work through instruction or otherwise, for in so doing they will incur contractual duties. This would be outside the skillset of most domestic clients, would not be covered by the proper insurance and would be an imprudent course to pursue.

A domestic client duty summary sheet is included in the Appendices.

4.4 Designer

The design process contributes greatly to the success or otherwise of health and safety management. Not only do the majority of designers act as professional advisors to their client but they are also influentially placed to affect health and safety management outcomes by their role in the design development process.

Best practice design should always contribute to the effective delivery of health and safety outcomes, for it is enshrined in the by-laws of numerous design-related institutions. As such it is an implicit deliverable of good practice and owes more to the fulfillment of a best practice standard than to the imposition of legal requirements.

Hence, the design response as per the CDM Regulations 2015 and its earlier versions is simply an endorsement and extension of that acceptable standard. Whilst there is the need for demonstrable accountability in the discharge of legal duties, compatible with the requirements of these Regulations, it is crucial to appreciate that the core business of design delivery must be retained, now supported but not enslaved, by related management support systems.

The designer should be able to rely on his numerous design office procedures and in-house protocols, which together provide evidence of the discharge of his duties. The demonstrable visibility of the design process has never rested with a single

---

[18] Regulation 7(2) and 7(3).

proforma or tabulation, but has always had recourse to a selection of the following design office procedures and protocols:

- agenda items
- design office manuals
- design philosophy statements
- design reports
- design risk assessments
- minutes of meetings, e.g.
  - brainstorming sessions
  - coordination meetings
  - design review meetings
  - scoping of works
  - value–cost exercises
  - cost-benefit analysis
- modelling
  - computer flow analysis
  - three and four dimensional
- notes on drawings
- proformas
- progress photographs
- project risk registers
- sequence drawings
  - three dimensional
  - four dimensional
- sequential erection statements
- tabulations
- etc.

This accountability does not translate into an essay-style response with all t's crossed and i's dotted, for it is by reference to the previous listing, either selectively or collectively depending on the focus of the specific project, that the design team has always been able to demonstrate statutory compliance in the design management process and its incremental development at all stages.

Health and safety design risk management, as an integrated subset of design project management, delivers that accountability by such an evidential trail, and throughout offers a salient and focused insight to the

- identification
- appraisal
- contribution
- communication

of relevant health and safety issues.

The design radar screen should be switched on initially and continually tuned in to capture the unfolding and comprehensive catalogue of health and safety issues associated with the development of the project. After the relevant dutyholders, in the course of the design risk management process, have exercised their duties as regards the general principles of prevention[19] in accordance with the term 'so far as is reasonably practicable',[20] the final communication of relevant information[21] should be based on the assumption that all associated professional dutyholders are competent or have structured teams where everyone is competent or under the supervision of a competent person.[22]

This latter perspective is critical to the delivery of essential residual hazard information, for there is no benefit in the communication of information which a competent designer or contractor would expect to deal with on every project. If this is the approach, irrelevant information is being peddled and information overload ensures that key messages escape the recipient. It is often this lack of pragmatic focus that can generate the plethora of irrelevant paperwork and open the design process up to the critical charge that it is a bureaucratic paper-chase.

This underlines one of the philosophical foundation stones inherent in compliance with the CDM Regulations, which requires all dutyholders to become better communicators. Communication failure remains the one common aspect of project management failure, within and between teams. Communication should be succinct, project specific and focused on significant issues beyond those that could be expected to be dealt with on any similar project.

However, this approach must also be accompanied by political awareness which addresses those issues that are the strategic concern of the HSE in their periodic campaigns.

The design risk management perspective is based on foreseeability. This ensures that the relevant list of health and safety design-related issues is never time-barred and continues to expand in accordance with the development of the design process. The list of foreseeable health and safety issues grows throughout the design period, benefitting from proactive contribution from within the integrated team.

As with all project management responses, early identification provides a better time window for an expeditious and legally compliant resolution to hazard management.

The quality of the process can eventually be measured by decision-making which filters out irrelevant content from associated narratives.[23] The documents produced stand as partial evidence of the acceptable discharge of the dutyholder's role, or alternatively as an indictment of the entire process.

The design team must ensure that foreseeable[24] health and safety risk is eliminated, reduced or controlled through the design contribution, with the design team's focus being based on the holistic perspective that embraces aspects of buildability, constructability, operability and maintainability, right up to and inclusive of the demolition process.

---

[19] Refer Regulations 9(2) and 9(3).

[20] Refer Regulation 9(2).

[21] Refer Regulation 9(4).

[22] Refer Regulations 8(1), 8(2) and 15(7).

[23] E.g. Pre-construction information, construction phase plan and the health and safety file.

[24] Foreseeability relates not to what has actually been foreseen but to that which *should have* been foreseen as a result of the duties being discharged.

The challenge for the design team is appreciation of the constructability perspective, avoiding the imposition of methodology onto the contractor. Since the essence of contracting is based on the contractor's prerogative to undertake the work as he chooses providing that this has no detrimental effect on the permanent structure, it is essential that the design process provides information and not instruction. The latter should be a fallback position that only arises from operational necessity. For the designer to go beyond providing information and to instruct has immediate implications for professional indemnity insurance, as well as raising issues directly challenging professional competence.

The Regulations encourage the earliest dialogue between designer and contractor,[25] and whilst there is much benefit to be gained from 'early contractor involvement' and/or 'design and build' arrangements, numerous other procurement strategies exist which are not so supportive of this arrangement. Nonetheless, the earliest contractor-focused input to the design process is recommended, based on mutual professional respect, in order to facilitate true appreciation of constructability-related issues.

Health and safety aspects of design risk management should be evident in every facet of design development, with the greatest opportunities for contribution being in the early stages of the project. The process of health and safety design risk management must be implicit throughout every design stage from inception/feasibility onwards. It cannot be left as an afterthought or as a predetermined afternoon session. The design professional should remain vigilant of the fact that health and safety has always been an essential part of every element of the design process, irrespective of legislative demands.

Health and safety issues are not meant to dominate the design process, for they are but one integrated subset of issues alongside other design facets such as form, function, fitness for purpose, environmental impact and cost. All require due consideration.

Hence, the conditional statement 'so far as is reasonably practicable' allows professional judgment to be exercised, in acknowledgement of the design team's influence on the holistic team's overall contribution.

Design duties apply both to permanent and temporary works design teams, who must all discharge duties arising from the same regulations. Indeed temporary works design can be as innovative and challenging as permanent design and must not operate outside the statutory requirements.

The design function itself can be embraced by contractors, principal contractors, specialist contractors, architects, consulting engineers, quantity surveyors, interior designers temporary works engineers, chartered surveyors, technicians or anyone who specifies or alters a design. This latter point ensures that clients can also function as designers.

Note: It is the integrated team that delivers success, with the design team central to the effectiveness of the process. Fragmentation and isolation remain distractions and their disruptive possibility requires the vigilance of all parties.

A designer duty summary sheet is included in the Appendices.

Table 4.3: Designer duties, provides the detailed narrative.

---

[25] Refer Regulations 9(4), 13(2), 13(5), 15(4)(a).

Table 4.3 Designer duties

No.	Reg.	Regulation	Commentary	Stage
	2(1)	Defines designer as *any person (including a client, contractor or other person referred to in these Regulations) who in the course or furtherance of a business—* *(a) prepares or modifies a design; or* *(b) arranges for, or instructs, any person under their control to do so,* *relating to a structure, or to a product or mechanical or electrical system intended for a particular structure, and a person is deemed to prepare a design where a design is prepared under their control* *and design as including* *drawings, design details, specifications and bills of quantities (including specification of articles or substances) relating to a structure, and calculations prepared for the purpose of a design.*		
7		**Application to domestic clients**		
1	7(2)	*If a domestic client fails to make appointments required by regulation 5—* *(a) the designer in control of the pre-construction phase of the project is the principal designer.*	In such cases the designer could well be fulfilling principal designer duties. Ensure that such duties are not being taken on unknowingly by default.	Throughout the project.
8		**General duties**		
2	8(1)	*A designer (including a principal designer) or contractor (including a principal contractor) appointed to work on a project must have the skills, knowledge and experience and, if they are an organisation, the organisational capability, necessary to fulfil the role that they are appointed to undertake, in a manner that secures the health and safety of any person affected by the project.*	This is now the wider and more pragmatic view of the pedigree and qualifications of any appointee covered before the CDM Regulations 2015 by the term 'competent'.	Prior to appointment and throughout the project.
3	8(2)	*A designer or contractor must not accept an appointment unless they fulfil the conditions in paragraph (1).*	This is a self-certification statement and the appointed party must be able to furnish evidence of the fulfilment of the conditions above.	Prior to appointment.
4	8(3)	*A person who is responsible for appointing a designer or contractor to carry out work on a project must take reasonable steps to satisfy themselves that the designer or contractor fulfils the conditions in paragraph (1).*	This applies to all parties who are making appointments, all of whom must ensure that the dutyholders they appoint 'have the skills, knowledge and experience and, if they are an organisation, the organisational capability, necessary to fulfil the role that they are appointed to undertake, in a manner that secures the health and safety of any person affected by the project', as per Regulation 8(1).	Prior to appointment and preferably prior to the invite to tender and throughout the project.

(Continued)

Table 4.3 (Continued)

No.	Reg.	Regulation	Commentary	Stage
			Designer duties	
5	8(4)	*A person with a duty or function under these Regulations must cooperate with any other person working on or in relation to a project at the same or an adjoining construction site to the extent necessary to enable any person with a duty or function to fulfil that duty or function.*	Although the cooperative direction is towards those at the same or adjoining construction sites, the perspective needs to focus on the external environment because work other than on the construction site itself could compromise/be compromised by someone else's management arrangements. Note the greater duty of care arising out of acts or omissions.	Throughout the project. A changing situation that has to be revisited with appropriate regularity to identify all cooperating parties.
6	8(5)	*A person working on a project under the control of another must report to that person anything they are aware of in relation to the project which is likely to endanger their own health and safety or that of others.*	This is the 'duty of care' enshrined in the Health and Safety at Work etc. Act 1974.	Throughout the project.
7	8(6)	*Any person who is required by these Regulations to provide information or instruction must ensure the information or instruction is comprehensible and provided as soon as practicable.*	The prompt supply of information/instruction is a critical prerequisite of communication. Account must be taken of the requirement that such information should be provided in a form that can be understood by all relevant parties, all of whom must be managed effectively.	Prior to the need for such information and throughout the project. Such a need should be established well in advance. Note the distinction between the dutyholder obligation to provide information generally and the dutyholder duty to provide specific information under Reg. 9(4).
9		**Duties of designers**		
8	9(1)	*A designer must not commence work in relation to a project unless satisfied that the client is aware of the duties owed by the client under these Regulations.*	This is to ensure that the client is fully immersed in the process. Particular attention should be paid to the client's ongoing duties under Regulation 4(1) and 4(3). Standard proforma letters are often issued or the matter dealt with in the initial meeting and the response captured in the minutes. The client's response could also signify the level of support required by him to fulfil his duties. **Note:** there are no exceptions to this.	Prior to commencement of work. On multi-disciplinary design projects this is best left to the principal designer to avoid a surplus of similar letters being delivered to the 'busy' client, but assurances should be sought that this has been done and the fact captured in the minutes of the relevant meeting.

9	9(2)	When preparing or modifying a design the designer must take into account the general principles of prevention and any pre-construction information to eliminate, so far as is reasonably practicable, foreseeable risks to the health and safety of any person— (a) carrying out or liable to be affected by construction work; (b) maintaining or cleaning a structure; or (c) using a structure designed as a workplace.	The general principles of prevention, i.e. elimination and/or reduction and/or communication, in compliance with the term 'so far as is reasonably practicable', form the full response mode of the designer in the management of health and safety issues associated with the project. This process must be demonstrable. At the start of any project every designer is entitled to receive relevant historical background information about the site from either the client or the principal designer under the guise of pre-construction information.	Throughout all design stages.
10	9(3)	If it is not possible to eliminate these risks, the designer must, so far as is reasonably practicable— (a) take steps to reduce or, if that is not possible, control the risks through the subsequent design process; (b) provide information about those risks to the principal designer; and (c) ensure appropriate information is included in the health and safety file.	Similar information should be provided to every designer in accordance with his design function in the project. **Note:** for some specialised work packages containing a design and construct element, such appointments come late into the project, but relevant information is still required.	Throughout the design process.
11	9(4)	A designer must take all reasonable steps to provide, with the design, sufficient information about the design, construction or maintenance of the structure, to adequately assist the client, other designers and contractors to comply with their duties under these Regulations.	Information to be promptly provided and is meant to focus on project-specific information of a significant nature. As a result of the design process, relevant information could be required as inputs to the following processes: • pre-construction information • construction phase plan • health and safety file. **Note:** all design work should confront the question as to whether, as a result of the design, an amendment/alteration/ modification is required to any existing health and safety file which the client has a duty to maintain up to date.	Throughout the design process.

(Continued)

4 Dutyholders

Table 4.3 (Continued)

No.	Reg.	Regulation	Commentary	Stage
		Designer duties		
	10	**Designs prepared or modified outside Great Britain**		
12	10(1)	Where a design is prepared or modified outside Great Britain for use in construction work to which these Regulations apply— (a) the person who commissions it, if established within Great Britain; or (b) if that person is not so established, the client for the project, must ensure that regulation 9 is complied with.	Overseas-based designers are appointed by others and there is a duty to ensure that the person who appoints, if established in Great Britain, must ensure that such teams understand and discharge their duties under Regulation 9. The advent of large design conglomerates now ensures that this is a greater possibility.	To be established in advance of such appointments, which could occur at numerous points dependent on procurement strategy. Documentary evidence would need to be evident in the discharge of this duty. Focused workshops can offer assurances.

Note:

1. Inadvertently many clients take on design duties through over-involvement in the design process. Care needs to be exercised by the client, who should be guided by his professional team.
2. A single designer could well take on principal designer duties since the appointment of the latter is only dependent on there being more than one contractor foreseen at any time during the construction stage.
3. Designer duties apply regardless of whether there is a client or not.
4. Designer duties apply to both permanent works design and temporary works design.

4.5 Principal designer

This is a pivotal role created under the CDM Regulations 2015 and is one of only two statutory appointments that have to be made by the client[26] (in writing) on any construction project where it is foreseeable that there will be more than one contractor working on site at any time during the construction phase.

The principal designer is in part a successor to the planning supervisor under the CDM Regulations 1994 and the CDM coordinator appointed under the CDM Regulations 2007, both of which have now been rendered obsolete. It would be imprudent, however, to consider the position as a direct replacement, since dutyholder interfaces have changed, the continuum of interaction has been extended and process management demands altered.

Historical association with its predecessors still mistakenly links this role with the larger project, whilst in reality it is a client-appointed role, now divorced from the notification process and dependent only on the foreseeability of there being more than one contractor on site at any one time. This translates into the principal designer function being undertaken on many smaller projects, simply because of the two-contractor scenario.

Thus, a wider range of projects, from the relatively small project right through to the multi-million pound, multi-disciplinary megaproject, will now have a principal designer as a project team member. The principal designer management model must therefore be flexible and capable of adapting in order to discharge related duties across its portfolio of varied projects and must be guided by the words *appropriateness* and *proportionate* throughout.

The principal designer manages the health and safety aspects of the pre-construction stage of the project and has essential interaction with the client, designers, principal contractor (and contractors) at key project stages. He is a creature of the Regulations, preferably appointed early by the client, with a duty to assist the client in the provision of pre-construction information.[27] His role is greatly facilitated by client support, for he is a statutory appointment and not a contractual appointment and therefore cannot take contractual action directly against non-compliant parties. However, it should be noted that his function is derived from the statutory instrument, which gives it a weighting above both civil and contract law.

The function demands visibility and team-member integration and depends on effective inter-personal skills and continuing dialogue with other dutyholders. It could be delivered by the individual on the smaller project although on the more complex project it is preferable to see it as a team-based function with compatible resource provision.

Whilst Regulation 5(1) requires such an appointment to be made 'as soon as is practicable, and, in any event, before the construction phase begins', it is beneficial for this appointment to be made as early as possible because of the principal designer's influential position, in concert with the design process, in delivering optimal health and safety management outcomes in the early design stages.

Debate continues over the pedigree of the principal designer, and it is worth noting that the original predecessor (planning supervisor followed by CDM coordinator) was never visualised by Nattrass[28] as a service to be delivered by any party other than the construction professional, with a further stipulation that in his opinion it should not give rise to a separate discipline.

---

[26] Regulation 5(1).
[27] Regulation 11(6)(a).
[28] Stuart Nattrass: Chief Inspector of Construction at the HSE and Chairman of CONIAC, 1994.

In the interim, numerous interest groups have moved into delivering that service, partly because of the void created by professional inertia and partly because of the income-stream possibilities provided. It must also be acknowledged that in the early days most construction- and design-related tertiary education courses gave inadequate coverage to the health and safety content of syllabi and thus the construction professional in any discipline was indeed disadvantaged.

The twenty-year window since the original launch of the Regulations has seen change, with tertiary education syllabi duly responding to industry's needs by constructive criticisms offered by CONIAC[29] et al.; organisational promotion by ICE and other learned societies; awareness enhancement by the CITB[30] etc.; and strategic promotion by the likes of APS[31] and ICS.[32]

The Regulations state that the principal designer 'means the designer appointed under Regulation 5(1) to perform the specified duties in regulations 11 and 12'. The definition of designer[33] is itself not specific and little guidance is given elsewhere on the pedigree desirable in any appointment, other than the requirements of Regulation 8(1).[34]

There are undoubted benefits in the principal designer coming from a design background and having a design-related qualification, but the role does not rest exclusively on that pedigree. A basic requirement is that there is an understanding of and working insight into the design and construction processes as well as pragmatic appreciation of the CDM Regulations 2015 and other construction-related legislation. This opens up the opportunity for delivery to numerous construction parties, which is needed to account for the complexity of project detail.

The pedigree of the principal designer for the two-contractor project will differ greatly from the pedigree required on the multi-disciplinary megaproject. Prudence must be exercised, since over-qualification and unfocused demands could well lead to additional on-costs, greater resource provision, bureaucratic mismanagement and an unnecessary, unhelpful burden of response on the expanding portfolio of smaller projects.

Two further arguments persist. The first concerns the design team itself and whether it is best placed to fulfil this vital function. Such an arrangement favours Nattrass's earlier vision, provides continuity through the design stages, provides a favourable structure for team integration and offers the one-stop scenario favoured by many clients. However, there is a danger of losing objectivity through close proximity to the design process and considerable reluctance to accept this additional responsibility has been encountered in design professionals. This latter point carries validity in terms of resource compatibility but is spurious in terms of technical and managerial positioning, since the design process must implicitly consider the health and safety issues inherent throughout design, regardless of the role of the principal designer.

---

[29] Construction Industry Advisory Committee.

[30] Construction Industry Training Board.

[31] Association for Project Safety.

[32] Institution of Construction Safety.

[33] Designer means 'any person (including a client, contractor or other person referred to in these Regulations) who in the course or furtherance of a business—(a) prepares or modifies a design; or (b) arranges for, or instructs, any person under their control to do so'.

[34] Regulation 8(1): 'A designer (including a principal designer) or contractor (including a principal contractor) appointed to work on such a project must have the skills, knowledge and experience, and, if they are an organisation, the organisational capability, necessary to fulfil the role that they are appointed to undertake, in a manner that secures the health and safety of any person affected by the project.'

The second argument relates to the appointment of the third-party principal designer, which, due to his independence, counters some of the concerns above but positions the role further away from the design process, giving rise to valid concerns over full team integration. This argument can be overcome by professionalism and the establishment of philosophical alignment with the intent of the Regulations prior to appointments being made.

As always, successful projects are delivered by those with the right attitude. There will always be choice in the manner in which appointments are made and the principal designer could therefore be an integral member of the design team, a third-party independent appointment, or even be appointed as a result of a sub-consultancy agreement between a design team and their chosen party, undertaking health and safety management coordination on their behalf.

However, it is only the client who can appoint the principal designer, and such appointment must be in writing and made at the appropriate time. Appointments must be devoid of flagrant self-interest and for the benefit of the project at large, based ultimately on valid and sensible criteria.

The person occupying the role manages and coordinates the responsibilities of other team members to ensure that significant and foreseeable health and safety risks are managed throughout the project via the design process. The role is ongoing, and continues from the concept and feasibility stages, through detailed design, into the construction phase and generally up to the compilation and handover of the health and safety file.

* * * * * * * * * * * * * * * * * *

The principal designer role must also account for procurement strategy and can be conveniently transferred by the client to different parties as the project proceeds, as for example, through its shell and core, fit-out and landscape phases. Such arrangements, however, will continue to pose continuity challenges.

In a 'design and build' project, the initial design contribution would invariably be undertaken by the designer contracted by the client, who would be well positioned to function as the principal designer. After the subsequent appointment of the principal contractor the original designer becomes novated[35] to the principal contractor, with the latter now managing the design process. This provides an argument for the principal designer role to be undertaken, going forward, by the principal contractor, although other arrangements can be agreed. However, since it is only the client who can appoint, any such change must be actioned by the client.

Client transfer of the role could also be initiated by concerns over the efficacy of management arrangements arising out of the client's obligation under Regulation 4(3),[36] and the resulting need to reappoint a party who will continue to function competently throughout the project.

A principal designer summary sheet is included in the Appendices.

Table 4.4: Principal designer duties, provides the detailed narrative.

---

[35] Novation is a common agreement in construction and engineering projects, particularly in relation to design and build procurement, where design consultants' appointments are transferred from the employer to the contractor in line with the contractor's single point of design responsibility.

[36] Regulation 4(3): 'A client must ensure that these management arrangements are maintained and reviewed throughout the project.'

4 Dutyholders

Table 4.4 Principal designer duties

No.	Reg.	Regulation	Commentary	Stage
Principal designer duties				
1	2(1)	Defines principal designer as *the designer appointed under regulation 5(1)(a) to perform the specified duties in regulations 11 and 12* with the designer himself defined as *any person (including a client, contractor or other person referred to in these Regulations) who in the course of furtherance of a business—* *(a) prepares or modifies a design, or* *(b) arranges for, or instructs, any person under their control to do so.*		
	7	**Application to domestic clients**		
2	7(1)	*Where the client is a domestic client the duties in regulations 4(1) to (6) and 7 must be carried out by—* *(c) the principal designer where there is a written agreement that the principal designer will fulfil those duties.*	This is one of three options that could arise.	Such client duties need to be established before the project starts and fulfilled throughout the project phases.
3	7(2)	*If a domestic client fails to make appointments required by regulation 5—* *(a) the designer in control of the pre-construction phase of the project is the principal designer*	In such cases the principal designer's role could be fulfilled by the single designer. Ensure that such duties are not being taken on unknowingly by default.	Throughout the project.
	8	**General duties**		
4	8(1)	*A designer (including a principal designer) or contractor (including a principal contractor) appointed to work on a project must have the skills, knowledge and experience and, if they are an organisation, the organisational capability, necessary to fulfil the role that they are appointed to undertake, in a manner that secures the health and safety of any person affected by the project*	This is now the wider and more pragmatic view of the pedigree and requirements of any appointee covered before the CDM Regulations 2015 by the term 'competent'.	Prior to appointment and throughout the project.
5	8(2)	*A designer or contractor must not accept an appointment unless they fulfil the conditions in paragraph (1).*	For designer read principal designer – this is a self-certification statement and the appointed party must be able to furnish evidence of the fulfilment of the conditions above or decline the appointment.	Prior to appointment.

6	8(3)	A person who is responsible for appointing a designer or contractor to carry out work on a project must take reasonable steps to satisfy themselves that the designer or contractor fulfils the conditions in paragraph (1).	This also infers the principal designer and applies to all parties who are making appointments, all of whom must ensure that the dutyholders they appoint 'have the skills, knowledge and experience and, if they are an organisation, the organisational capability, necessary to fulfil the role that they are appointed to undertake, in a manner that secures the health and safety of any person affected by the project', as per Regulation 8(1).	Prior to appointment and preferably prior to the invite to tender.
7	8(4)	A person with a duty or function under these Regulations must cooperate with any other person working on or in relation to a project at the same or an adjoining construction site to the extent necessary to enable any person with a duty or function to fulfil that duty or function.	Although the cooperative direction is towards those on the project and on adjoining construction sites, the perspective needs to focus on the wider external environment because work other than on the construction site itself could compromise/be compromised by management arrangements. Note the greater duty of care arising out of acts or omissions.	Throughout the project. A changing situation that has to be revisited with appropriate regularity to identify all cooperating parties.
8	8(5)	A person working on a project under the control of another must report to that person anything they are aware of in relation to the project which is likely to endanger their own health and safety or that of others.	This is the 'duty of care' enshrined in the Health and Safety at Work etc. Act 1974.	Throughout the project.
9	8(6)	Any person who is required by these Regulations to provide information or instruction must ensure the information or instruction is comprehensible and provided as soon as practicable.	The prompt supply of information/instruction is a critical prerequisite of communication. Account must be taken of the requirement that such information should be provided in a form that can be understood by all relevant parties, all of whom must be managed effectively.	Prior to the need for such information and throughout the project. Such a need should be established well in advance and identified in content and expected time of delivery. Note the distinction between the dutyholder obligation to provide information generally and the dutyholder duty to provide specific information. Refer Reg. 9(4).
10	8(7)	To the extent that they are applicable to a domestic client, the duties in paragraphs (3), (4) and (6) must be carried out by the person specified in regulation 7(1).	On the domestic client project, client duties could be fulfilled by the principal designer provided a written agreement is entered into with the client. However, the party fulfilling client duties needs to be established.	Before involvement in the project. Regulation 7(1).

4 Dutyholders

(Continued)

Table 4.4 (Continued)

No.	Reg.	Regulation	Commentary	Stage
10		**Designs prepared or modified outside Great Britain**		
11	10(1)	Where a design is prepared or modified outside Great Britain for use in construction work to which these Regulations apply— (a) the person who commissions it, if established within Great Britain; or (b) if that person is not so established, the client for the project, must ensure that regulation 9 is complied with.	Since, dependent on procurement strategy, principal designers sometimes appoint overseas-based designers, there could be a duty to ensure that such teams understand and discharge their duties under Regulation 9. This depends on the appointing party being established in Great Britain, otherwise this becomes a client duty. The advent of large design conglomerates now ensures that this is a greater possibility. Principal designer advice and assistance to the client is helpful here.	To be established in advance of such appointments, which could occur at numerous points dependent on procurement strategy. Documentary evidence would need to be evident in the discharge of this duty. Focused workshops can offer assurances.
11		**Duties of a principal designer in relation to health and safety at the pre-construction phase**		
12	11(1)	The principal designer must plan, manage and monitor the pre-construction phase and coordinate matters relating to health and safety during the pre-construction phase to ensure that, so far as is reasonably practicable, the project is carried out without risks to health and safety.	It is the monitoring that is the critical factor here, since planning and managing relies on predictive assumptions and controls. The monitoring rigour then allows action to be taken when the reality differs from the assumption.	Throughout all stages of the project.
13	11(2)	In fulfilling the duties in paragraph (1), and in particular when— (a) design, technical and organisational aspects are being decided in order to plan the various items or stages of work which are to take place simultaneously or in succession; and (b) estimating the period of time required to complete such work or work stages, the principal designer must take into account the general principles of prevention and, where relevant, the content of any construction phase plan and health and safety file.	This is to ensure that health and safety management controls, as based on information provided in the pre-construction process and as developed in the articulated response in the construction phase plan, have taken account of the general principles of prevention, and remain dynamic and effective for the duration of the project. **Note:** the general principles of prevention require the following hierarchy to be exercised in the management of risk namely: elimination reduction or minimisation, and the communication of residual hazard information to relevant parties based on the discharge of those duties in accordance with the term 'so far as is reasonably practicable'.	Throughout all stages of the project.
14	11(3)	In fulfilling the duties in paragraph (1), the principal designer must identify and eliminate or control, so far as is reasonably practicable, foreseeable risks to the health and safety of any person— (a) carrying out or liable to be affected by construction work; (b) maintaining or cleaning a structure; or (c) using a structure designed as a workplace.	In essence, unless the principal designer is also a designer, the role here would be to ensure that the other design teams have adopted this hierarchal approach. Since the thrust of the above is contained in Regulation 11(4), Regulation 11(3) requires the principal designer to manage the organisation of design health and safety risk management.	Throughout all stages of the project.

15	11(4)	*In fulfilling the duties in paragraph (1), the principal designer must ensure all designers comply with their duties in regulation 9.*	This requires a proactive interface with all the relevant design teams and for the largest projects would require a coordination model accounting for the multi-disciplinary complexity of the numerous design teams. Standardisation of approach and commonality of proformas and project (health and safety) risk registers would greatly facilitate the outcome.	Throughout all stages of the project, which must also account for the approach of the temporary works designers working for the contractor(s).
16	11(5)	*In fulfilling the duty to co-ordinate health and safety matters in paragraph (1), the principal designer must ensure that all persons working in relation to the pre-construction phase cooperate with the client, the principal designer and each other.*	Cooperation and coordination are cornerstones of effective communication. The list of those parties with whom cooperation is required changes throughout all stages of a project. The list therefore needs regular updating and re-distribution.	Throughout the project. **Note:** the pre-construction phase could extend well beyond the start of construction in any project.
17	11(6)	*The principal designer must—* *(a) assist the client in the provision of the pre-construction information required by regulation 4(4); and* *(b) so far as it is within the principal designer's control, provide pre-construction information, promptly and in a convenient form, to every designer and contractor appointed, or being considered for appointment, to the project.*	Since the pre-construction information process often starts before the principal designer is appointed, the principal designer on appointment needs to establish the status quo of information (provided and awaited) and advise the client accordingly. The expectation would then be that the principal designer distributes the information to those designers and contractors entitled to receive it.	The receipt of such information is not time-barred and updates/additions/amendments could well be distributed at necessary intervals.
18	11(7)	*The principal designer must liaise with the principal contractor for the duration of the principal designer's appointment and share with the principal contractor information relevant to the planning, management and monitoring of the construction phase and the coordination of health and safety matters during the construction phase.*	The principal designer therefore acts as a conduit between the design and construction stages. Critical to this function is the assurance that design change has been communicated and that the principal contractor's construction phase plan has duly responded, accounting for the constraints within the construction programme.	From appointment of both parties and throughout the construction phase.
12		**Construction phase plan and health and safety file**		
19	12(3)	*The principal designer must assist the principal contractor in preparing the construction phase plan by providing to the principal contractor all information the principal designer holds that is relevant to the construction phase plan including—* *(a) pre-construction information obtained from the client;* *(b) any information obtained from designers under regulation 9(3)(b).*	Such information focuses on the residual hazards which should have been identified in the project. Usually it is the pre-construction information (tender stage) that collectively houses all the relevant information and therefore it is important that this document is received at an appropriate time. However, later communication of relevant information would also be a requirement.	The pre-construction information (tender stage) should be received prior to tendering so that the contents can be appreciated and resource compatibility allowed for in the tender price submitted.

(Continued)

Table 4.4 (Continued)

			Principal designer duties	
No.	Reg.	Regulation	Commentary	Stage
20	12(5)	*During the pre-construction phase, the principal designer must prepare a health and safety file appropriate to the characteristics of the project which must contain information relating to the project which is likely to be needed during any subsequent project to ensure the health and safety of any person.*	Since the health and safety file eventually becomes a client document, early dialogue is necessary between principal designer and client to establish the requisite form and format for its delivery. The process management of the health and safety file must be visible throughout and information collected and collated as and when it should be available. It would be a mistake to wait until the latter stages of a project, because of the possibility of the disappearing dutyholder.	
21	12(6)	*The principal designer must ensure that the health and safety file is appropriately reviewed, updated and revised from time to time to take account of the work and any changes that have occurred.*	Hence the process of health and safety file compilation is a dynamic factor of the project.	From principal designer appointment and throughout the project.
22	12(7)	*During the project, the principal contractor must provide the principal designer with any information in the principal contractor's possession relevant to the health and safety file, for inclusion in the health and safety file.*	The content of a health and safety file is dependent on relevant inputs, one of which is from the principal contractor, who collates the relevant items from the various contractors. Information should be provided as and when it becomes available. Other input streams would be from the client and other designers.	Throughout the construction phase. Such information and delivery dates should be established between the principal contractor and the principal designer at the earliest possible stage.
23	12(8)	*If the principal designer's appointment concludes before the end of the project the principal designer must pass the health and safety file to the principal contractor.*	This represents a disconnect in the health and safety file management process and is not ideal. Such a possibility should provide for an overlapping handover arrangement between the principal designer and the principal contractor. Alternatively, the principal designer by arrangement could be commissioned to extend his role until the handover of the health and safety file.	Such a possibility should be identified at the tender stage and communicated during pre-construction information. Parties should be informed accordingly.

24	12(9)	*Where the health and safety file is passed to the principal contractor under paragraph (8), the principal contractor must ensure that the health and safety file is appropriately reviewed, updated and revised from time to time to take account of the work and any changes that have occurred.*	The handover point is critical here with attention directed at the expected and actual content of the health and safety file. Good communication is vital between the principal designer and principal contractor to ensure the security of the client's long-term interests Particular attention focused on the period leading up to the document exchange and for the period thereafter until handover.
25	12(10)	*At the end of the project, the principal designer, or where there is no principal designer, the principal contractor, must pass the health and safety file to the client.*	This actual point of handover is ill-defined and the 'end of the project' delivery date must be accounted for on a project-by-project basis. The actual handover date should be agreed between the client and principal designer and/or principal contractor before the start of the project.

Note:
1. Regulation 12 requires the principal designer to manage the preparation of a health and safety file. There will undoubtedly be projects that because of their nature will not deliver any relevant content into a meaningful health and safety file. However, the health and safety file management process must still be demonstrably visible to provide evidence that this lack of content was the sensible conclusion.
2. The management and preparation of the health and safety file must be visible and demonstrable throughout the entire involvement of the principal designer so that, in the event of lack of information provision, the reasonable, competent approach of the principal designer can be demonstrated.

4 Dutyholders

4.6 Contractor

Contractors operate at the exposed edge of construction and have always made up the major proportion of site fatalities and associated occupational ill-health and disease statistics. They are too often used, not for their skill and expertise, but as a financial buffer to smooth out the vagaries of cash-flow irregularity. They remain vulnerable in a process that can seek to transfer risk instead of managing it and end up with no option but to deal with the issues handed down by others, who themselves are risk averse, but nonetheless are often better positioned to effectively contribute. The 'general principles of prevention' were never the sole domain of the contractor, but have an implication for all dutyholder team members.

Figures for the last ratifiable year[37] identify a welcome fall in construction deaths, down to 35 fatalities plus 4 members of the public, which also provides the lowest recorded incident rate of 1.62 per 100,000 workers (1.98 the previous year and a five-year average of 2.7).

Such figures however do not include the 40% of approximately 4,000 additional construction fatalities per year associated with asbestos-related deaths. Such a perspective ensures that there can never be room for complacency.

As a result of their function, the contractor and specifically the sub-contractor are positioned way down the supply chain and must manage the residual risks after other dutyholders have effectively discharged their duties. However, the findings of *Research Report 218*[38] provide a haunting perspective for all construction professionals:

> almost half of all accidents in construction could have been prevented by designer intervention and ... at least 1 in 6 of all accidents are at least partially the responsibility of the lead designer in that opportunities to prevent accidents were not taken.

The report also identified that

> In many instances contractor design incompetence was a major contributor to an accident.

Whilst the contributory equation is complex, it is to be hoped that the statistical reductions now being experienced remain longstanding and are indicative of better communication, technical improvements, heightened awareness, integrated team ethos and industry-wide cultural advancements made over the last twelve years, since that report was published.

The fulfillment of duties must continue unabated and without compromise, for the restraining considerations of project cost and time limits remain only as boundary conditions to be complied with and cannot be used as mitigation in respect of non-compliance.

It is a construction truism that the lack of a health and safety incident should never be taken as evidence of a robust management control system, for without rigorous systems of continuous review, update and revision, the adverse outcome is merely waiting in the shadows for further victims.

These Regulations endorse the extended management responsibility now imposed on the single contractor by the need to produce construction phase plans on all projects, regardless of project size, cost or duration. This now becomes the responsibility of either the single contractor or the principal contractor on a multi-contractor project.

---

[37] To 31 March 2015, but remaining provisional until adjustments are made up to July 2016.

[38] Research Report 218, *Peer review of analysis of specialist group reports on causes of construction accidents*, prepared by Habilis Ltd for the Health and Safety Executive 2004.

This should not be seen as burdensome, for it is little more than the compliant contractor should have been delivering prior to the 2015 Regulations, via his response to the management regulations[39] and other construction-related legislation.

It is essential that the principles of *appropriateness* and *proportionality* remain paramount in providing guidance as to the form and format of this key, site-based document.[40] A commonsense approach to the provision of the necessary and the abandonment of the excessive is of critical importance in the day-to-day pragmatic delivery of health and safety compliance. All construction professionals contribute, with managerial judgment dictating meaningful responses that unambiguously deliver controls over health and safety enhancement rather than generating irrelevant, unhelpful paperwork.

Since 1 January 1993, the management regulations have required workplace risk assessments and method statements as standard approaches to the management control of workplace activities. This remains the essential content of any construction phase plan, and, together with a valid outline of infrastructure details, such as roles and responsibilities, contact details, site induction, emergency provision and welfare arrangements, completes the narrative for the smaller project. Complex projects need a more rigorous approach, with resource pedigree and managerial experience compatible with the need to deliver the more robust response.

The strength of the management control model as represented by the construction phase plan is dependent on the ability to respond through the continuous revision and update process. This is a vital exercise, since planning and method statements attempt to predict the foreseeable, with an informed awareness that reality differs from prediction. The limitations of the process must be appreciated and documents must be continually monitored to ensure the promotion and efficacy of the control system. A team response is demanded and encouraged by the statutory need to communicate relevant issues up and down the management spine, as required by Regulation 14.[41]

The establishment of a harmonious and effective dialogue between the appropriate dutyholders, from the earliest opportunity, greatly facilitates the process. The contractor's (or principal contractor's) project-specific construction phase plan should be based on relevant pre-construction information provided either by the client or principal designer and derived from relevant background and historical sources. The author of this construction phase plan (whether contractor or principal contractor) and the arbiter under Regulations 4(1)(a) and 10(6) (either the client or the principal designer) must strive to deliver a meaningful and useful facilitation of health and safety management control.

Additional to the requirement for a construction phase plan on all projects is the statutory need for the appointment by the client of a principal contractor as a prerequisite on projects where it is foreseeable that there will be more than one contractor working at any time during the construction phase. Thus, the appointment is to be made before the construction phase begins. No project should move into its construction phase unless each contractor is aware of who is fulfilling the principal contractor role.

The titular nature of this role is familiar from both the 1994 and 2007 versions of the Regulations but in scale and detail it will be less exacting, although nonetheless

---

[39] The Management of Health and Safety at Work Regulations 1999 outline what employers are required to do to manage health and safety under the Health and Safety at Work Act. The Regulations apply to every work activity.

[40] HSE publication, Construction Phase Plan (CDM 2015), CIS80, published by HSE, and the CITB app 'CDM Wizard', freely downloadable.

[41] Regulation 14: 'Principal contractor's duties to consult and engage with workers.'

essential on the smaller project. The small contractor will already be familiar with the bulk of obligations through his successful management of projects to date in compliance with existing construction-related legislation.

Legislative change under Regulation 5(1)[42] will dictate that many smaller contractors will have opportunities to work as principal contractors, in closer liaison with the principal designer, who must also be appointed by the client on the multi-contractor site. This is to enhance coordination and management control during the construction phase and should not be problematic once the detail of discharge is appreciated (refer section 4.7: Principal Contractor). The requirement for this function must be established by the client and his professional advisors before the construction phase starts.

Occasionally, the foreseeability of there being more than one contractor is only clarified after the start of the construction phase, as scope change and quantifiable risk appreciation becomes more finely tuned. Whilst this situation is to be avoided, this is not always possible, and belated appointments ensue. This dilemma could well result in the client unwittingly fulfilling the principal contractor[43] (and principal designer) duties in the early construction phase to the detriment of professional relationships and the possibility of exposure to the legal process. Wherever possible the more conservative approach is to be championed.

A contractor duty summary sheet is included in the Appendices.

Table 4.5: Contractor duties, provides the detailed narrative.

4.7 Principal contractor

One of the fundamental changes incorporated into the CDM Regulations 2015 now links the appointment of the principal contractor (and principal designer) to the foreseeability of there being more than one contractor at any one time during the construction phase. Unlike previous versions of these Regulations, such appointments are not dependent on the notification process. Principal contractors will therefore be required on many more projects than previously, simply because of this multiple-contractor stipulation.

The principal contractor is a client appointment (except by default of the client, whether commercial[44] or domestic[45]), made in writing, whose role is to coordinate the construction phase work so that it is managed effectively in matters of health and safety management. This is a situation that must be determined before the start of the construction phase and ideally much earlier to facilitate the essential 'constructability' dialogue between principal contractor and principal designer. Ideally the latter would be appointed in advance of the principal contractor appointment.

Both are statutory appointments, to be made no later than the start of the construction phase. However, such last-minute timing, whilst legally compliant, is not helpful for project success or for the achievement of CDM management aims, since at that stage:

- design would be well advanced
- opportunities for change incur greater cost as the project develops

---

[42] Regulation 5(1): 'Where there is more than one contractor, or if it is reasonably foreseeable that more than one contractor will be working on a project at any time, the client must appoint in writing—(b) a contractor as principal contractor.'

[43] Regulation 5(4): 'If the client fails to appoint a principal contractor, the client must fulfil the duties of the principal contractor in regulations 12 to 14.' Similarly in respect of the appointment of the principal designer under Regulation 5(3).

[44] Regulation 5(4).

[45] Regulation 7(2)(b).

Table 4.5 Contractor duties

		Contractor duties	
No.	**Reg.**	**Regulation**	**Commentary**	**Stage**
	2(1)	Defines contractor as *any person (including a non-domestic client) who, in the course or furtherance of a business, carries out, manages or controls construction work*		
		Note: 1. Since there are no further definitions, the one-person contractor and the large organisation directly employing hundreds of operatives would both be defined as a contractor. This has implications for the number of contractors on site at any one time. 2. Pre-construction information must be provided by the client to every contractor to be appointed. On a multi-contractor site this would usually be provided to the principal contractor by the client and/or the principal designer and then distributed by him accordingly.		
7		**Application to domestic clients**		
1	7(1)	*Where the client is a domestic client the duties in regulations 4(1) to (7) and 6 must be carried out by* (a) *the contractor for a project where there is only one contractor*	This is one of three options that could arise.	Such client duties need to be established before the project starts and fulfilled throughout the project phases.
2	7(2)	*If a domestic client fails to make appointments required by regulation 5 —* (b) *the contractor in control of the construction phase of the project is the principal contractor.*	In such cases the contractor could well be fulfilling principal contractor duties. Ensure that such duties are not being taken on unknowingly by default.	Throughout the project.
8		**General duties**		
3	8(1)	*A designer (including a principal designer) or contractor (including a principal contractor) appointed to work on a project must have the skills, knowledge and experience and, if they are an organisation, the organisational capability, necessary to fulfil the role that they are appointed to undertake, in a manner that secures the health and safety of any person affected by the project.*	This is now the wider and more pragmatic view of the pedigree and requirements of any appointee covered before the CDM Regulations 2015 by the term 'competent'.	Prior to appointment and throughout the project.
4	8(2)	*A designer or contractor must not accept an appointment unless they fulfil the conditions in paragraph (1).*	This is a self-certification statement and the appointed party must be able to furnish evidence of the fulfilment of the conditions above or decline the appointment.	Prior to appointment.

(Continued)

4 Dutyholders

Table 4.5 (Continued)

No.	Reg.	Contractor duties		Stage
		Regulation	Commentary	
5	8(3)	*A person who is responsible for appointing a designer or contractor to carry out work on a project must take reasonable steps to satisfy themselves that the designer or contractor fulfils the conditions in paragraph (1).*	This also applies to all parties who are making appointments, all of whom must ensure that the dutyholders they appoint 'have the skills, knowledge and experience and, if they are an organisation, the organisational capability, necessary to fulfil the role that they are appointed to undertake, in a manner that secures the health and safety of any person affected by the project' as per Regulation 8(1).	Prior to appointment and preferably prior to the invite to tender and throughout the project.
6	8(4)	*A person with a duty or function under these Regulations must cooperate with any other person working on or in relation to a project at the same or an adjoining construction site to the extent necessary to enable any person with a duty or function to fulfil that duty or function.*	Although the cooperative direction is towards those on adjoining construction sites, the perspective needs to focus on the external environment because work other than on the construction site itself could compromise/be compromised by someone else's management arrangements. Note the greater duty of care arising out of acts or omissions.	Throughout the project. A changing situation that has to be revisited with appropriate regularity to identify all cooperating parties.
7	8(5)	*A person working on a project under the control of another must report to that person anything they are aware of in relation to the project which is likely to endanger their own health and safety or that of others.*	This is the 'duty of care' enshrined in the Health and Safety at Work etc. Act 1974.	Throughout the project
8	8(6)	*Any person who is required by these Regulations to provide information or instruction must ensure the information or instruction is comprehensible and provided as soon as practicable.*	The prompt supply of information/instruction is a critical prerequisite of communication. Account must be taken of the requirement that such information should be provided in a form that can be understood by all relevant parties, all of whom must be managed effectively. Note the distinction between the dutyholder obligation to provide information generally and the dutyholder duty to provide specific information under Reg. 9(4).	Prior to the need for such information and throughout the project. Such a need should be established well in advance.
9	8(7)	*To the extent that they are applicable to a domestic client, the duties in paragraphs (3), (4) and (6) must be carried out by the person specified in regulation 7(1).*	If there is only one contractor on a domestic client project then the client duty would be legally imposed on the single contractor.	Regulation 7(1).

	10	**Designs prepared or modified outside Great Britain**	
10	10(1)	*Where a design is prepared or modified outside Great Britain for use in construction work to which these Regulations apply—* (a) *the person who commissions it, if established within Great Britain; or* (b) *if that person is not so established, the client for the project, must ensure that regulation 9 is complied with.*	Since contractors sometimes appoint overseas-based designers, there could be a duty to ensure that such teams understand and discharge their duties under Regulation 9.This depends on the appointing contractor being established in Great Britain, otherwise it becomes a client duty. The advent of large design conglomerates now ensures that this is a greater possibility.	To be established in advance of such appointments, which could occur at numerous points dependent on procurement strategy. Documentary evidence would need to be evident in the discharge of this duty. Focused workshops can offer assurances.
	15	**Duties of contractors**	
11	15(1)	*A contractor must not carry out construction work in relation to a project unless satisfied that the client is aware of the duties owed by the client under these Regulations.*	Best done via a proforma letter or as an agenda item in the pre-start meeting with the affirmed answer captured in the minutes. There are no exceptions.	Prior to starting construction work. On larger projects this is best left to the principal contractor to avoid a surplus of similar letters being delivered to the 'busy' client. However, assurances should be sought that this has been done, and the response captured in the minutes of the relevant meeting.
12	15(2)	*A contractor must plan, manage and monitor construction work carried out either by the contractor or by workers under the contractor's control, to ensure that, so far as is reasonably practicable, it is carried out without risks to health and safety.*	Health and safety management arrangements must be adequately set up from the start and remain effective throughout the project.	**Before the start and throughout the project. The adage 'PLAN LONGER BUILD SAFER AND QUICKER' carries a resonant message for every contractor.**
13	15(3)	*Where there is more than one contractor working on a project, a contractor must comply with—* (a) *any directions given by the principal designer or the principal contractor; and* (b) *the parts of the construction phase plan that are relevant to that contractor's work on any project*	The contractor must comply with the relevant parts of the construction phase plan and directions given by the principal contractor and the principal designer. This latter point is contentious for the route to the contractor has always been via the principal contractor. This protocol should be maintained for continuity of communication and good management practice. Subsection (b) is dependent on the provision of relevant information by the principal contractor and access to such information.	Throughout the construction phase. Regulations 3(1) and 14(c).

(Continued)

Table 4.5 (Continued)

No.	Reg.	Regulation	Contractor duties		Stage
			Commentary		
14	15(4)	*If there is only one contractor working on the project, the contractor must take account of the general principles of prevention when—* *(a) design, technical and organisational aspects are being decided in order to plan the various items or stages of work which are to take place simultaneously or in succession; and* *(b) estimating the period of time required to complete the work or work stages.*	The general principles of prevention vis-à-vis elimination, reduction or minimisation, and the final communication of residual hazards, as evidenced in the detail of each risk assessment and workplace method statement. Appropriate health and safety resource compatibility must dictate all working operations.		Throughout the construction phase.
15	15(5)	*If there is only one contractor working on the project, the contractor must draw up a construction phase plan, or make arrangements for a construction phase plan to be drawn up, as soon as is practicable prior to setting up a construction site.*	For the single contractor a construction phase plan must always be drafted. In other situations (multiple contractor sites) it would be drafted by the principal contractor.		Before construction start and updated throughout the construction phase in accordance with the programme of works.
16	15(6)	*The construction phase plan must fulfil the requirements of regulation 12(2).*	Construction phase plan must appropriately articulate the detail of health and safety management controls.		Throughout the construction period. **Note:** this document, at every stage, is the culmination of a proactive exercise of management control, which is always ahead of the corresponding site activities (other than in emergency situations).
17	15(7)	*A contractor must not employ or appoint a person to work on a construction site unless that person has, or is in the process of obtaining, the necessary skills, knowledge, training and experience to carry out the tasks allocated to that person in a manner that secures the health and safety of any person working on the construction site.*	All persons employed must have the necessary skills, knowledge, training and experience to work safely and healthily or be under the supervision of someone who has that appropriate level of skills, knowledge, training and experience.		Skills must be gained prior to employment; otherwise an appointee must work under supervision throughout the project. **Note:** it is the team that must demonstrate these characteristics rather than the one individual.
18	15(8)	*A contractor must provide each worker under their control with appropriate supervision, instruction and information so that construction work can be carried out, so far as is reasonably practicable, without risks to health and safety.*	Achieved through site management arrangements, induction processes, construction phase plan abstracts, tool-box talks etc.		Throughout the construction phase.

19	15(9)	The information provided must include—	Reference to the Management Regulations is a reference to the Management of Health and Safety at Work Regulations 1999 and also includes the 2003 amendment (which removes the civil liability exclusions from the original).	Prior to the start of work on site and at suitable intervals thereafter. Consider the need for re-induction when there is a related change to the construction site environment.
		(a) a suitable site induction, where not already provided by the principal contractor;		
		(b) the procedures to be followed in the event of serious and imminent danger to health and safety;	These regulations were introduced to reinforce the Health and Safety at Work etc. Act 1974, and place duties on employers and employees including clients, designers, principal contractors and other contractors.	
		(c) information on risks to health and safety:		
		(i) identified by the risk assessment under regulation 3 of the Management Regulations, or		
		(ii) arising out of the conduct of another contractor's undertaking and of which the contractor in control of the worker ought reasonably to be aware; and	Whilst many of the duties overlap with the CDM Regulations, they do go beyond, especially in the case of expectant mothers and young people.	
		(d) any other information necessary to enable the worker to comply with the relevant statutory provisions.		
20	15(10)	A contractor must not begin work on a construction site unless reasonable steps have been taken to prevent access by unauthorised persons to that site.	The site must be secure against trespassers regardless of levels of vandalism.	From day one and throughout the entire construction phase. Any breaches require immediate remedial action.
21	15(11)	A contractor must ensure, so far as is reasonably practicable, that the requirements of Schedule 2 are complied with so far as they affect the contractor or any worker under that contractor's control.	Schedule 2 sets out the 'Minimum welfare facilities required for construction sites'.	From day one of the construction phase and effectively maintained throughout the construction period.

Note:

1. Construction sites must also account for the health and safety of both invited and uninvited guests. Part 4: 'General requirements for all construction sites' takes account of this, with further duties existing under the Occupiers Liability Act 1984.

2. Contractors can also take on designer duties through 'Lump sum' design arrangements, or more frequently, via temporary works design.

- constructability/buildability issues are not fully appreciated

- vital principal designer and principal contractor dialogues remain unspoken

- there will be adverse reflection on project ethos

- team integration is not promoted.

As a result of the two-contractor criteria premeditating the appointment of the principal contractor, a greater number of smaller contractors will be encouraged to take on this key management role. For the smaller project, the requirement should not deter the competent contractor from responding to the challenge, which is based on coordination and control rather than the generation of additional and irrelevant paperwork. All construction projects must have a construction phase plan, and therefore the function of principal contractor ensures due coordination of the process between contractors, with the responsibility falling to one designated party to exercise overall management control, thus avoiding ambiguity and providing communicative continuity. The appointment must be made before the start of construction, regardless of when the second contractor appears on site.

A distinction must be made between the differing management challenges for the principal contractor on the two-contractor site and the same role on the more complex multi-disciplinary project. It is this continuum of principal contractor responsibility that now presents the challenge. Appropriateness and proportionality must prevail and the management models must remain fit for purpose, without the need for unnecessary paperwork. It is obvious that such control requirements would generate different management models to account for the greater robustness and rigour inherent in the more complex situation.

Commonsense must prevail between the parties to ensure the principal contractor response is appropriate to the nature of the project and the management of its associated hazards. There is a concern that failure to appreciate the less than subtle changes to the scoping of the principal contractor's role across the range of potential situations will again lead to the bureaucratic nightmare scenario, as inappropriate documentation is showered onto the smaller project. The principal contractor and client must re-focus on the full extent of this role and ensure that it is configured to account for effective delivery across the wider range of projects.

The role is undertaken at the sharp end of the construction project, where health and safety management is crucial to the establishment and maintenance of safe and suitable conditions of work, as precursors of successful project delivery. For the principal contractor, it entails the health and safety management and coordination of all activities involved in the delivery of the construction phase of the project, without the direct supervision of each group of contractors.

The principal contractor arrangements should deliver management control through the proactive demonstration of:

- leadership
- effective communication
- good supervision
- efficacy of coordination and cooperation
- commitment
- clear decision making
- organisational abilities

achieved by:

- effective process control systems
- succinct and focused construction phase plan narratives
- ongoing monitoring and review
- consistency
- liaison
- consultation with the workforce
- continuous improvement
- resource compatibility
- meaningful dialogue.

One anomaly arising out of the Regulations relates to the definition of contractor, which can range from the single operative to an organisation directly employing hundreds of operatives across several disciplines. It is obvious that in this latter case, with only the one large contractor on site, there would not be a statutory need for the client to appoint a principal contractor. The absence of a second contractor pre-empts the need for a principal designer appointment as per Regulation 5(1)(a), despite the fact that for the larger project there is likely to be the involvement of multi-disciplinary design teams.

Nonetheless, the management structure required to effectively coordinate and control the health and safety-related issues on such a project would require an appropriate level of sophistication akin to the roles fulfilled by the principal contractor and principal designer.

It is to be remembered that compliance is the baseline, with the raising of management standards to a best-practice benchmark encouraged, with benefits accruing to all dutyholders.

Whilst there is only one principal contractor on a project at any one time, the client could re-designate the role to another contractor in accordance with the procurement strategy or reappoint due to concerns about the ability of the first appointment to successfully perform the role.

The principal contractor is the author of the construction phase plan,[46] which must be appropriately developed before the start of the construction phase. There is immediate interaction between principal contractor and principal designer through the provision of pre-construction information,[47] which is the springboard for the collation of the construction phase plan, and with the client[48] who must concern himself with the suitability of this document prior to commencement of any work on site.

Thereafter, it is the statutory duty of the principal contractor to develop the construction phase plan compatible with the programme of works and relevant design changes that occur over the project duration. The principal contractor's interface with the client continues throughout, since the client must at all times be satisfied with the management arrangements via obligations under Regulation 4(3). This could be facilitated by the client's professional team on his behalf, but should not translate into the hands-on appraisal of the construction phase plan through

---

[46] Refer section 6.3.
[47] Refer section 6.2.
[48] Regulations 4(1), 4(5)(a), 12(4).

its subsequent development, other than ensuring that such development is indeed happening. A corresponding and ongoing site progress meeting agenda item would normally suffice.[49]

A principal contractor duty summary sheet is included in the Appendices.

Table 4.6: Principal contractor duties, provides the detailed narrative.

---

[49] Refer Appendices: Effective Management Arrangements.

Table 4.6 Principal contractor duties

No.	Reg.	Regulation	Commentary	Stage
	2(1)	Defines principal contractor as the contractor appointed under regulation 5(1)(b) to perform specified duties in regulations 12 to 14.		
	7	**Application to domestic clients**		
1	7(1)	Where the client is a domestic client the duties in regulations 4(1) to (6) and 7 must be carried out by— (b) the principal contractor for a project where there is more than one contractor	This is one of three options that could arise.	Such client duties need to be established before the project starts and fulfilled throughout the project phases.
2	7(2)	If a domestic client fails to make appointments required by regulation 5— (a) the contractor in control of the construction phase of the project is the principal contractor.	This is still dependent on the foreseeability of there being more than one contractor on the project at any one time. Ensure that such duties are not being taken on unknowingly by default.	Such a duty needs to be established before the project starts and fulfilled throughout the construction phase.
	8	**General duties**		
3	8(1)	A designer (including a principal designer) or contractor (including a principal contractor) appointed to work on a project must have the skills, knowledge and experience and, if they are an organisation, the organisational capability, necessary to fulfil the role that they are appointed to undertake, in a manner that secures the health and safety of any person affected by the project	This is now the wider and more pragmatic view of the pedigree and requirements of any appointee covered before the CDM Regulations 2015 by the term 'competent'.	Prior to appointment and throughout the project.
4	8(2)	A designer or contractor must not accept an appointment unless they fulfil the conditions in paragraph (1).	This is a self-certification statement and the appointed party must be able to furnish evidence of the fulfilment of the conditions above or decline the appointment.	Prior to appointment.
5	8(3)	A person who is responsible for appointing a designer or contractor to carry out work on a project must take reasonable steps to satisfy themselves that the designer or contractor fulfils the conditions in paragraph (1).	This also infers the principal contractor and applies to all parties who are making appointments, all of whom must ensure that the dutyholders they appoint 'have the skills, knowledge and experience and, if they are an organisation, the organisational capability, necessary to fulfil the role that they are appointed to undertake, in a manner that secures the health and safety of any person affected by the project', as per Regulation 8(1).	Prior to appointment and preferably prior to the invite to tender and throughout the project.

(Continued)

4 Dutyholders

Table 4.6 (Continued)

No.	Reg.	Regulation	Principal contractor duties — Commentary	Stage
6	8(4)	A person with a duty or function under these Regulations must cooperate with any other person working on or in relation to a project at the same or an adjoining construction site to the extent necessary to enable any person with a duty or function to fulfil that duty or function.	Although the cooperative direction is towards those on the project and on adjoining construction sites, the perspective needs to focus on the wider external environment because work other than on the construction site itself could compromise/be compromised by management arrangements. Note the greater duty of care arising out of acts or omissions.	Throughout the project. A changing situation that has to be revisited with appropriate regularity to identify all cooperating parties.
7	8(5)	A person working on a project under the control of another must report to that person anything they are aware of in relation to the project which is likely to endanger their own health and safety or that of others.	This is the 'duty of care' enshrined in the Health and Safety at Work etc. Act 1974.	Throughout the project
8	8(6)	Any person who is required by these Regulations to provide information or instruction must ensure the information or instruction is comprehensible and provided as soon as practicable.	The prompt supply of information/instruction is a critical prerequisite of communication. Account must be taken of the requirement that such information should be provided in a form that can be understood by all relevant parties, all of whom must be managed effectively. **Note:** failure to effectively communicate is the one common thread of project failure.	Prior to the need for such information and throughout the project. Such a need should be established well in advance and content and expected time of delivery identified.
9	8(7)	To the extent that they are applicable to a domestic client, the duties in paragraphs (3), (4) and (6) must be carried out by the person specified in regulation 7(1).	Ensure that these duties are not inadvertently imposed.	Before involvement in the project. Regulation 7(2)(b).
10	10	**Designs prepared or modified outside Great Britain**		
10	10(1)	Where a design is prepared or modified outside Great Britain for use in construction work to which these Regulations apply— (a) the person who commissions it, if established within Great Britain; or (b) if that person is not so established, the client for the project, must ensure that regulation 9 is complied with.	Since, dependent on procurement strategy, principal contractors sometimes appoint overseas-based designers, there could be a duty to ensure that such teams understand and discharge their duties under Regulation 9. This depends on the appointing party being established in Great Britain; otherwise it becomes a client duty. The advent of large construction conglomerates now ensures that this is a greater possibility.	To be established in advance of such appointments, which could occur at numerous points dependent on procurement strategy. Documentary evidence would need to be evident in the discharge of this duty. Focused workshops can offer assurances.

		Duties of a principal designer in relation to health and safety at the pre-construction phase	
11			
11	11(6)	*The principal designer must—* *(b) so far as it is within the principal designer's control, provide pre-construction information, promptly and in a convenient form, to every designer and contractor appointed, or being considered for appointment, to the project.*	Pre-construction information must be provided by the principal designer to the principal contractor for the purposes of producing the construction phase plan. In that sense it should be provided at the tender stage, since it contains relevant information which must be accounted for in the tender price submitted through the inclusion of resource compatibility costs necessary to manage the associated hazards. The receipt of such information is not time-barred and updates/additions/ amendments could well be distributed at necessary intervals.
12	11(7)	*The principal designer must liaise with the principal contractor for the duration of the principal designer's appointment and share with the principal contractor information relevant to the planning, management and monitoring of the construction phase and the coordination of health and safety matters during the construction phase.*	This represents a vital link between the pre-construction phase and the construction phase and a continuous dialogue between principal contractor and principal designer remains critical throughout. Critical to this function is the assurance that design change has been communicated and that the principal contractor's construction phase plan has duly responded, taking into account constraints within the construction programme. From appointment of both parties and throughout the construction phase.
12		**Construction phase plan and health and safety file**	
13	12(1)	*During the pre-construction phase, and before setting up a construction site, the principal contractor must draw up a construction phase plan or make arrangements for a construction phase plan to be drawn up.*	The construction phase plan is the key control document in respect of the construction phase and should articulate with the necessary detail the management controls for delivering the safe and suitable procedures corresponding to the construction activities. Suitably prepared prior to the start of construction and developed thereafter, in accordance with the programme of works, and accounting for all relevant design change. Regulation 12(4).
14	12(2)	*The construction phase plan must set out the health and safety arrangements and site rules, taking account, where necessary, of the industrial activities taking place on the construction site and, where applicable, must include specific measures concerning work which falls within one or more categories set out in Schedule 3.*	Schedule 3 highlights construction work carrying particular risks and is a reduced portfolio of activities previously articulated under Item 3(a) of Appendix 3 (Construction phase plan) found in the ACoP to the CDM Regulations 2007. For Schedule 3 listings refer bottom of this tabulation.

(Continued)

4 Dutyholders

Table 4.6 (Continued)

No.	Reg.	Regulation	Principal contractor duties Commentary	Stage
15	12(3)	*The principal designer must assist the principal contractor in preparing the construction phase plan by providing to the principal contractor all information the principal designer holds that is relevant to the construction phase plan including—* *(a) pre-construction information obtained from the client;* *(b) any information obtained from designers under regulation 9(3)(b).*	Such information focuses on the residual hazards which should have been identified in the project. Usually it is the pre-construction information (tender stage) that houses all the relevant information and therefore it is important that this document is received at an appropriate time. However, later communication of relevant information would also be a requirement.	The pre-construction information (tender stage) should be received prior to tendering so that the contents can be appreciated and resource compatibility allowed for in the tender price submitted.
16	12(4)	*Throughout the project the principal contractor must ensure that the construction phase plan is appropriately reviewed, updated and revised from time to time so that it continues to be sufficient to ensure that construction work is carried out, so far as is reasonably practicable, without risks to health and safety.*	The key word here is sufficient, since the construction phase plan must be sufficient before any construction work starts to allow early stage activities to be completed safely and suitably and then subsequently developed compatible with the ever-changing programme of works and associated design changes. **Note: Since the client has a duty to ensure that management arrangements are maintained and reviewed throughout the project, it would be prudent for his attention to be focused on the development state of the construction phase plan. This is the key construction phase document and its development would signal the effectiveness of health and safety management controls. It is a developing document that should contain the management control ahead of any corresponding construction activity.**	Before the start of the construction phase and further developed throughout the entire construction phase. Particularly before construction starts and at suitable intervals throughout the project, e.g. at every site progress meeting, etc.
17	12(7)	*During the project, the principal contractor must provide the principal designer with any information in the principal contractor's possession relevant to the health and safety file, for inclusion in the health and safety file*	The principal contractor must coordinate his contractors' input to the health and safety file. Such information should be identified via early discussions between principal contractor and principal designer.	Information to be obtained from contractors/sub-contractors should be identified as early as possible together with a date for anticipated delivery. Without the anticipated date management control will fail.
18	12(8)	*If the principal designer's appointment concludes before the end of the project the principal designer must pass the health and safety file to the principal contractor.*	This represents a disconnect in the health and safety file management process and is not ideal. Such a possibility should focus attention on the handover arrangement between the principal designer and the principal contractor, with attention given to content expectation and actuality, before the situation becomes irredeemable.	Such a possibility should be identified at the tender stage and the parties informed accordingly.

19	12(9)	*Where the health and safety file is passed to the principal contractor under paragraph (8), the principal contractor must ensure that the health and safety file is appropriately reviewed, updated and revised from time to time to take account of the work and any changes that have occurred.*	Particular attention focused on the period leading up to the document exchange and for the period thereafter until handover to the client. The handover point is critical here, with attention directed at the expected and actual content of the health and safety file. Good communication is vital between the principal designer and principal contractor to ensure the security of the client's long-term interests. **Note:** there are benefits in some situations of agreeing an extension to the principal designer's commission for the sole purpose of delivering the health and safety file.
20	12(10)	*At the end of the project, the principal designer, or where there is no principal designer, the principal contractor, must pass the health and safety file to the client.*	This actual point of handover is ill-defined and the 'end of the project' delivery date must be accounted for on a project-by-project basis. The actual handover date should be agreed between the client and principal designer and/or principal contractor before the start of the project.
	13	**Duties of a principal contractor in relation to health and safety at the construction phase**	
21	13(1)	*The principal contractor must plan, manage and monitor the construction phase and coordinate matters relating to health and safety during the construction phase to ensure that, so far as is reasonably practicable, construction work is carried out without risks to health and safety.*	The role is to manage the construction phase through the effective health and safety management of all parties involved in the construction activities. Everything that happens on the construction site is under the overall management of the principal contractor. This does not translate into him having to supervise all the specialist work activities Throughout the construction period, with emphasis on the rigour of his management systems in continually reviewing, updating and revising his management controls, so that safe and suitable conditions of work continue to be provided.
22	13(2)	*In fulfilling the duties in paragraph (1), and in particular when—* *(a) design, technical and organisational aspects are being decided in order to plan the various items or stages of work which are to take place simultaneously or in succession; and* *(b) estimating the period of time required to complete the work or work stages;* *the principal contractor must take into account the general principles of prevention.*	This is to ensure that health and safety management controls, as based on information provided in the pre-construction process and as developed in the construction phase plan, have taken account of the general principles of prevention and remain dynamic and effective for the duration of the project. **Note:** the general principles of prevention require the following hierarchy to be exercised in the management of risk: elimination, reduction or minimisation, and the communication of residual hazard information to relevant parties, those duties being discharged on the basis of the term 'so far as is reasonably practicable'. In this sense they extend to workplace activities and to any temporary works design or design elements specifically managed by the principal contractor.

(Continued)

4 Dutyholders

Table 4.6 (Continued)

No.	Reg.	Principal contractor duties		
		Regulation	Commentary	Stage
23	13(3)	The principal contractor must— (a) organise cooperation between contractors (including successive contractors on the same construction site); (b) coordinate implementation by the contractors of applicable legal requirements for health and safety; and (c) ensure that employers and, if necessary for the protection of workers, self-employed persons— (i) apply the general principles of prevention in a consistent manner, and in particular when complying with the provisions of Part 4; and (ii) where required, follow the construction phase plan.	Cooperation and coordination remain key words for effective communication and management. The principal contractor must ensure all health and safety legal requirements are complied with by all contractors, and remain satisfied that employers and self-employed persons apply the general principles of prevention, namely: elimination, reduction/minimisation and communication of residual issues, in accordance with the term 'so far as is reasonably practicable'. The management system of the principal contractor must ensure that the construction phase plan is being followed by all relevant contractors.	Throughout the construction phase. The list of those with whom cooperation is required changes throughout the project and so the contact list needs amendment as appropriate.
24	13(4)	The principal contractor must ensure that— (a) a suitable site induction is provided; (b) the necessary steps are taken to prevent access by unauthorised persons to the construction site; and (c) facilities that comply with the requirements of Schedule 2 are provided throughout the construction phase.	All operatives must be the subject of a suitable induction process. **Note:** the need for a re-induction compatible with critical changes to the site environment. Site to be secured at all times from trespass and action taken to address any areas vandalised. Schedule 2 outlines the 'Minimum welfare facilities required for construction sites' (refer note below).	a) Prior to starting work on site and at intervals of induction update as required afterwards; b) throughout the project; c) from construction day one and throughout the project.
25	13(5)	The principal contractor must liaise with the principal designer for the duration of the principal designer's appointment and share with the principal designer information relevant to the planning, management and monitoring of the pre-construction phase and the coordination of health and safety matters during the pre-construction phase.	The principal designer therefore acts as a conduit between the design and construction stages. Critical to this function is the assurance that design change has been communicated and that the principal contractor's construction phase plan has duly responded, taking account of the constraints within the construction programme. This is a two-way arrangement.	From appointment of both parties and throughout the construction phase.

14	**Principal contractor's duties to consult and engage with workers**	
26	**14**	*The principal contractor must—*	Cooperation and consultation are prerequisites for empowerment and engagement between management and the workforce.

(a) *make and maintain arrangements which will enable the principal contractor and workers engaged in construction work to cooperate effectively in developing, promoting and checking the effectiveness of measures to ensure the health, safety and welfare of the workers;*

(b) *consult those workers or their representatives in good time on matters connected with the project which may affect their health, safety or welfare, in so far as they or their representatives have not been similarly consulted by their employer;*

(c) *ensure that those workers or their representatives can inspect and take copies of any information which the principal contractor has, or which these Regulations require to be provided to the principal contractor, which relate to the health, safety or welfare of workers at the site, except any information—*

   (i) *the disclosure of which would be against the interests of national security;*

   (ii) *which the principal contractor could not disclose without contravening prohibition imposed by or under enactment;*

   (iii) *relating specifically to an individual, unless that individual has consented to its being disclosed;*

   (iv) *the disclosure of which would, for reasons other than its effect on health, safety or welfare at work, cause substantial injury to the principal contractor's undertaking or, where the information was supplied to the principal contractor by another person, to the undertaking of that other person;*

   (v) *obtained by the principal contractor for the purpose of bringing, prosecuting or defending any legal proceedings.*

This Regulation establishes the requirement of feedback from the working face to management, enabling controls to be refined and altered if found not to be working.

This is a vital and beneficial two-way communication link throughout all construction phases.

NOTE Schedule 3, 'Work involving particular risks', lists the following potential hazards associated with work:

1. Susceptible to earth falls; engulfment in swampland; falling from height and risk particularly aggravated by the nature of the work or associated processes or other environmental factors.

2. Susceptible to chemical or biological dangers and/or involving a legal requirement for health monitoring (Control of Substances Hazardous to Health (COSHH) 2002).

3. Affected by ionising radiation (Ionising Radiations Regulations 1999).

4. Near high voltage power lines.

5. Exposing workers to the risk of drowning.

6. On wells, underground earthworks and tunnels.

7. Carried out by divers requiring system of air supply.

8. Carried out by workers in caissons, with a compressed air atmosphere.

9. Involving the use of explosives.

10. Involving the assembly or dismantling of heavy prefabricated components.

NOTE Schedule 2/Document L153, 'Minimum welfare facilities required for construction sites' provides more detailed information on the following:

1. Sanitary conveniences.

2. Washing facilities.

3. Drinking water.

4. Changing rooms and lockers.

5. Facilities for rest.

4 Dutyholders

5 The design process

5.1 Introduction

The design risk management process drives health and safety contribution from the conceptual stage through all the intervening project stages up to and including demolition at the point of obsolescence. The process involves opportunities for contribution at the most opportune time throughout, and can exert great influence for the benefit of the project team and others who come into contact with the realisation of the process.

The Regulations do not require the designer to act in a divine function, but only to discharge his duties to the term 'so far as is reasonably practicable'. Other dutyholders must also discharge duties, governed by the same term. During the journey down the supply chain this usually translates as the management of residual hazards arising out of the design process, appreciating that the residual hazard platform is different for every dutyholder.

Compliance with the Regulations neither restricts the innovative design approach nor directs the process towards a narrow path, for there are numerous design solutions that can be legitimately pursued, all of which could signal the adequate discharge of duties.

At all times the designer is seeking to reach the optimal solution. For situations where that goal cannot be reached, more information will have to be communicated because of residual hazards that demand controlled management, details of which will need to pass down the supply chain, enabling the best-positioned party to take control. This does not represent non-compliance, although the optimal solution remains the team objective.

The pedigree of the design team as outlined in Regulation 8(1) is based on the prior acquisition of:

> the skills, knowledge and experience, and, if they are an organisation, the organisational capability, necessary to fulfil the role they are appointed to undertake ...

The content of Regulation 8(1) should also be compared with the content of regulation 15(7):

> A contractor must not employ or appoint a person to work on a construction site unless that person has, or is in the process of obtaining, the necessary skills, knowledge, training and experience to carry out the tasks allocated to that person in a manner that secures the health and safety of any person working on the construction site.

CDM Regulations 2015 Procedures Manual, Fourth Edition. Stuart D. Summerhayes.
© 2016 John Wiley & Sons, Ltd. Published 2016 by John Wiley & Sons, Ltd.

It should be apparent that it is the team that must have and exhibit the necessary collective facets of competence, with every team member either able to demonstrate all the characteristics or be under the supervision of such a person. If this is not the case, there will be no possibility of entry for the uninitiated.

This implicitly acknowledges the factors that the team collectively are expected to exhibit by virtue of the function they are fulfilling, taking account of market place technical information. This could well contrast with the limitations of support and library information and ensures that the pursuit of technical and professional appreciation is never-ending.

All dutyholders have to successfully respond to the term 'so far as is reasonably practicable'.[1]

The Court of Appeal's interpretation of this phrase is:

> Reasonably practicable is a narrower term than physically possible, and implies that a computation must be made in which the quantum of risk is placed in one scale, and the sacrifice, whether in money, time or trouble, involved in the measures necessary to avert the risk, is placed in the other; and that, if it be shown that there is a gross disproportion between them, the risk being insignificant in relation to the sacrifice, the person upon whom the duty is laid discharges the burden of proving that compliance was not reasonably practicable. This computation falls to be made at a point of time anterior to the happening of the incident complained of.

Despite the challenge of fully understanding the above text, the designer is allowed choice, based on his informed professional judgment. There are numerous options available for the pragmatic discharge of duties, with no single dictum pointing to one avenue of pursuit. The design risk management process is therefore subjective, influenced by professional judgment, industry norms, good practice and sectorial guidance.

Nonetheless, the argument in support of the outcome must be coherent, based on full awareness of health and safety related issues, and capable of demonstrating *consideration*, *contribution* and *communication*, as illustrated in Figure 5.1: Systems approach to the design process.

Health and safety outcomes are but one factor to be considered during the design risk management process and, whilst critical, they must not dominate the other considerations of form, function, fitness of purpose, aesthetics, environmental impact and cost, all of which are facets of the argument and considerations to be accounted for in the search for a viable design solution.

Visibility ensures that on every project the design team must be able to demonstrably answer the question

What is your contribution to health and safety management on this project?

The CIRIA Report 662[2] identifies a Hazard Elimination and Risk Reduction (HERR) strategy, at the heart of the design risk management approach, which follows a simple audit trail:

1. Identification

2. Evaluation

---

[1] *Edwards* v. *The National Coal Board*. Court of Appeal, 1949. In the health and safety context, the term 'reasonably practicable' is much older than the 1974 Health and Safety at Work Act.

[2] CIRIA publication C662: *Construction Design and Management 2007 (CDM 2007)*. *Construction Work Sector Guidance for Designers*. January 2007. ISBN 0860176622. To be superseded by CIRIA Report 755, anticipated late 2015.

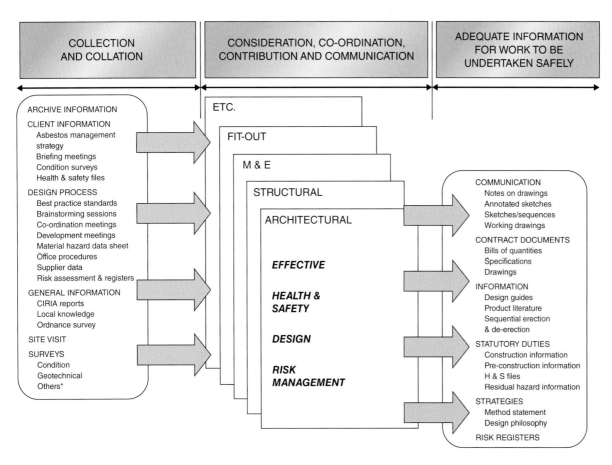

Figure 5.1 Systems approach to the design process.

3. Contribution

   (i)   Elimination

   (ii) Reduction/minimisation

   (iii) Communication

4. Monitor

5. *Review*

5.2 Identification

This is the first step in the health and safety risk management process, and if team members are unable to identify the issues through either ignorance or complacency, the subsequent process is flawed. It is vital not to embark on a generic approach (anathema to the HSE) for today's design team challenge is to think 'outside the box'. The checklist mentality ensures only that the designer becomes a prisoner of the checklist boundaries, which stifle creativity and health and safety management contribution. Nonetheless, the checklist as an 'aide memoire' is useful as a quality assurance exercise after the event.

Competency and baggage are inevitable partners and therefore identification of issues must rely on innovative thinking and brainstorming. Indeed, the brainstorming session offers the benefit of the collective experience and wisdom of the team, which is inevitably greater than that of the individual. This is a luxury not always available to the designer on the smaller project, but its benefits should be appreciated, as

5 The design process

should the fact that the objective, unfettered insight does not have to involve large team gatherings.

Failure to identify the issues at the appropriate time ensures that due consideration cannot be given, rendering the design risk management exercise limited by the narrower window of opportunity subsequently available. The entire sequence is ongoing and the foreseeability of issues depends on the development stage of the project. Such issues become factors of time and progress. The identification of issues as soon as practicable is imperative to ensure that health and safety contribution can be maximised in the available time period.

5.3   Evaluation

All evaluation processes are subject to challenge in respect of their validity in the process of design contribution. The method of hazard evaluation or appraisal after identification is not prescribed and can vary from the simple qualitative description high, medium or low to the quasi-numerical approach based on a ten x ten matrix, or similar, accounting for *likelihood* and *severity*. At best the matrix approach is only a crude ranking device, for it has no numerical rigour. Concerns have been expressed at the failure to appreciate that this is more a black art than a science and that the determination of whether a factor deserves a lower number than the one above is somewhat academic and meaningless.

The hazard must be identified in order for the process to deal with it. Over the intervening twenty years since the first introduction of the Regulations, the design process within the construction industry has tended to move away from the numerical matrix approach towards a more qualitative assessment, and in some cases omits this evaluation step altogether. There is no one method to be followed and the dutyholder is free to develop his own procedures.

More sophisticated methods can be used, including probabilistic methodologies, but these are infrequently required for mainstream design. What is critical is that the hazard is appropriately identified and the requisite contribution made, based on the general principles of prevention,[3] practicably delivered under the sub-headings described in the next sections.

5.4   Contribution

The design team is aware of the need to *identify* the issues, and, having identified them, the team is then constructively challenged to make a health and safety *contribution* based on the following hierarchal response enshrined in the general principles of prevention:

* elimination

* minimisation/reduction

* communication (of residual hazard information).

The awareness exercise that precedes contribution must embrace a valid appreciation of construction-related health and safety issues, be aligned to current HSE interventionist strategies, and attempt to contribute in pyramidal fashion to the principle 'so far as is reasonably practicable'.

---

[3]   Schedule 1 of the *Management of Health and Safety at Work Regulations 1999* (L21) published by HSE Books. ISBN 0717624889.

Paragraph 102 of document L153 advises that

> Identifying *insignificant* risks is not an effective way of alerting other dutyholders to the important design issues they need to know about. Designers should be able to demonstrate they have addressed only the *significant* risks.

Thus the radar screen of the designer must capture the comprehensive list of potential hazards associated with the project, whilst delivering finally hazard information from the perspective of *significant* risks. This term is subjective and the communicator must acknowledge the ambient state of the construction culture. In that sense there is an argument for expansion and for the conversion of focus to the *significant* and *principal* health and safety issues, which introduces a political perspective because it relates to the current construction culture at any moment in time.

5.5 Monitor/review

Project management controls require proactive responses as part of their dynamic processes. Procedures depend on individuals and teams to augment systems as well as responding to constant changes in information, circumstances and experience. Failure to respond ensures the decline and obsolescence of control systems.

Thus the design risk management cycle must provide feedback as part of the journey of constant improvement. Systems need to be checked for delivery and altered when signals and outcomes differ from those anticipated and intended. The principal contractor, as well as the design team members, has a role to play in this process.

* * * * * * * * * * * * * * * * * * * *

There is no legal requirement for the completion of any particular form, record or tabulation, but the prudent design team should always have evidence of their management systems. This is not an all- singing-all-dancing record, but simply a framework of process visibility. Management systems must support the design process in discharging legal duties without enslavement to an overly bureaucratic process.

There is no unique model for recording the design risk assessment process and it is influenced by the nature of the undertaking, working practices and project complexity. Where non-compliances are identified, as a result of internal audit, consideration should be given to fine-tuning existing systems, rather than looking to reinvent the wheel.

Designers have always considered inherent health and safety issues, since this is a given of good practice and a basic requirement underpinned by the by-laws of the associated learned societies. Design organisations should therefore be looking for the fine adjustment of existing management systems rather than wholesale revamping. Where the above premise does not exist then a more robust update exercise must ensue.

Design attention must focus on issues that the design team are in a position to influence, hence the need for a distinction between design risk assessment and workplace risk assessment, the latter being the domain of the contractor. Contractors expect to deal with residual hazards arising from the justifiable limitations of the design contribution, but they cannot be coerced to deal with a non-compliant, ineffective process of design delivery.

Process development over the last twenty years has seen a movement away from the limited *risk assessment* proforma, used extensively in the post-1994 period, towards the more industry reflective and sophisticated project risk register now favoured.

This has its origins in the identification of adverse events that could threaten the viability of outcomes in the finance, insurance and cost-control industries.

It has a broad pedigree, and it offers a suitable means of cataloguing the health and safety-related design risk management issues and outcomes throughout the project. In that sense, all dutyholders contribute, from client, through designer to contractor, and the insertion of information into the register mirrors the dynamic movement of project development and sits comfortably with the project team as a proven facilitation device.

The dutyholder input needs management control, which could rest with the principal designer/principal contractor or could come under the third-party control of the project manager. (See table 5.1).

Table 5.1 Project risk (health and safety) register

	PROJECT RISK (Health and Safety) REGISTER			
PROJECT: Office refurbishment		**DATE: Sometime**	**SHEET: 1 of 4**	**Rev.: A**
Activity	**Description**	**Hazard**	**Mitigation/controls**	**Ownership**	**Signed**	**Future action**	**Status**
Site clearance	Basement areas	Sharps and needles	Advance sweep	Client P Contractor	ABClose BC Done	Pre-start meeting P C Information C P Plan	Completed
Preparatory works	Floor tile adhesive Versatemp panels Ceiling tiles above bar	Asbestos	Remove (ceiling tiles & panels) Encapsulate (tile adhesive)	P Contractor	BC Done	P C Information C P Plan H&S File	Methodology awaited
Structure	Ad hoc repairs to nos 14/15 Structural integrity	Collapse	Structural inspection Sequential alterations	Designer P Contractor	FG Tuce BC Done	Str. Report P C Information C P Plan	Methodology awaited
	Steel columns & beams	Fire/Hot work	Bolted connections Full height stanchions	Designer P Contractor	FG Tuce BC Done	Specification C P Plan	Awaited
	External staircase	Falls from height Manual handling Access restrictions	Prefabricated sections Factory treatment Bolted connections	Designer P Contractor	FG Tuce BC Done	Specification P C Information C P Plan	Details awaited
	Rooflights (existing)	Falls from height	Remove and roof over	Designer	VD Rote	Drawing details P C Information C P Plan	Completed
Service provision	Service runs	Dust (respiratory disease)	Surface mounted behind dry lining	Designer P Contractor	GH Jay	P C Information C P Plan	Development of C P Plan
Maintenance	Roof work Glass cleaning	Falls from height Falling objects	Parapet rails Self-cleaning glass	Designer P Contractor FM Team	VD Rote BC Done Awaited	P C Information C P Plan H&S File	Strategy being developed

6 Documentation

6.1 Introduction

The range of documentation delivered as a result of the associated processes within the Regulations stands as evidence of the discharge of duties or conversely as an indictment of failure to fulfil such duties. Whilst each of the corresponding documents serves a distinct purpose, there is considerable overlap and interfacing between all of the dutyholders involved in contribution, collation and authorship, and thus all of the document management processes should be collectively viewed as a portfolio that depends on and contributes to the project's information trail.

The quality of the documentation should repel any suggestion of the historical and unacceptable bureaucratic paper-chase, with the document authors filtering out irrelevancy. The effectiveness of the content owes as much to what is kept out as to what is included, and whilst authorship reflects a strong element of subjectivity, adequate guidance is provided in the L153 appendices and other sources. This should enable a pragmatic focus to be maintained, which must counter any tendency to lapse into the excesses of the past, through the provision of succinct, focused and relevant information directed at the project specifics. Indeed, past excesses appear to illustrate a failure of managerial interpretation rather than standing as a commentary on the shortcomings of earlier versions of these Regulations.

Construction health and safety management is dependent on good communication within and between the holistic and integrated teams through an appreciation of shared philosophies. Documentation is one of the vehicles by which this can be achieved, although not the end in itself.

The three process-related documents, pre-construction information, the construction phase plan and the health and safety file, are not an exercise in document production per se, but must serve to inform and control, as well as to provide evidence of compliance in fulfillment of dutyholder roles. Fundamentally, they should also be part of a project-control process that provides managerial support, in contrast to the often-cited charge of managerial enslavement.

The challenge under these Regulations is to successfully collate and draft documentation for a wider range of construction projects than previously, whilst still maintaining the perspective of *appropriateness* and *proportionality*. Hence, although documentation titles are similar to those previously used, the narrative within must change to capture the current significance and the wider implications of their use. This must readily identify the complexity of project detail coupled with the common purpose and objectives to ensure that a simple approach for the smaller project is as compliant and purposeful as the sophisticated computerised system for the complex project.

CDM Regulations 2015 Procedures Manual, Fourth Edition. Stuart D. Summerhayes.
© 2016 John Wiley & Sons, Ltd. Published 2016 by John Wiley & Sons, Ltd.

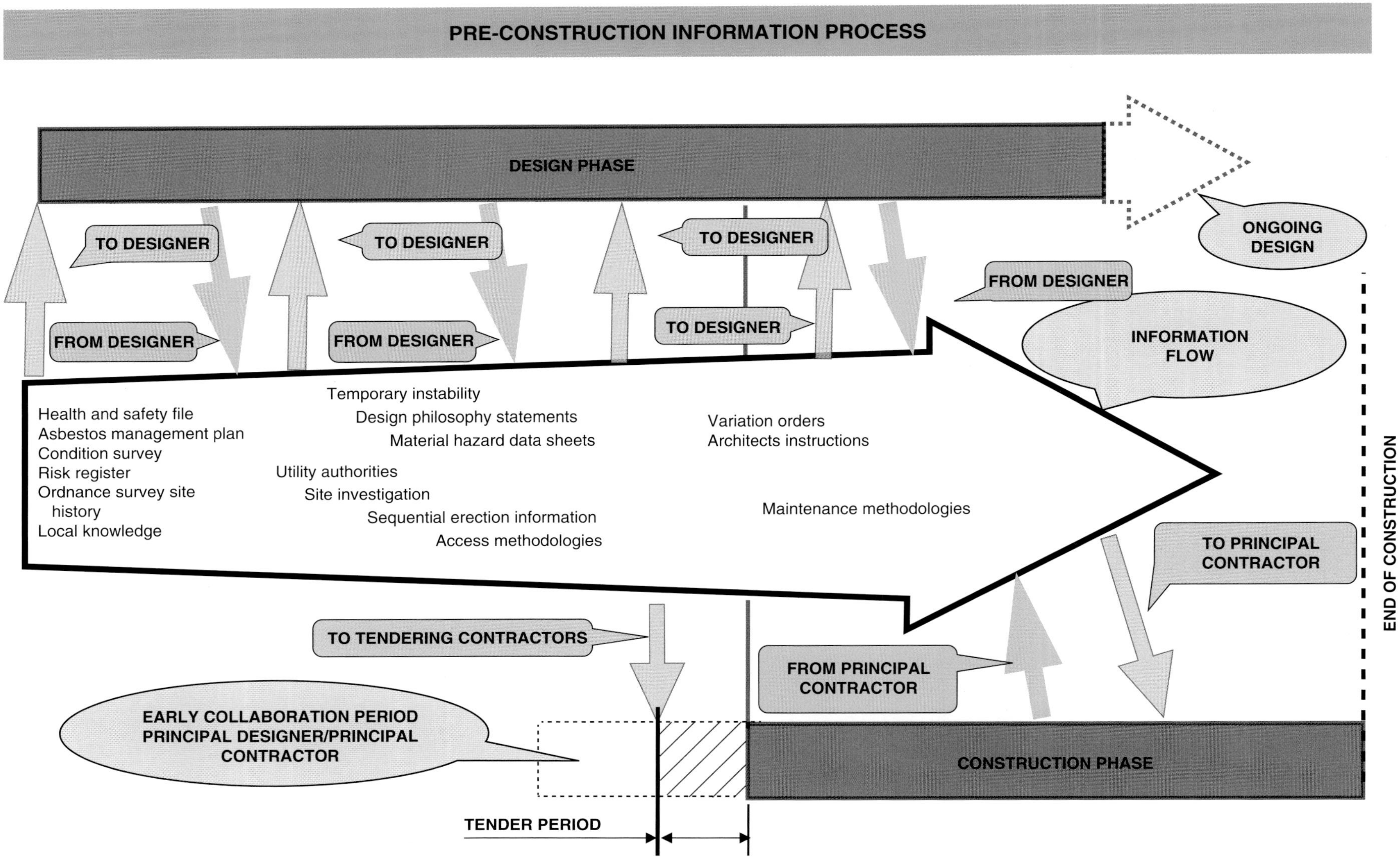

Figure 6.1 Information trail.

In conjunction with document management throughout, it is imperative that the dutyholder appreciates the true *purpose* of the documentation and continually strives to 'manage the risk and not the paperwork', subconsciously aware of Stuart Nattrass's[1] enduring words at the launch of the 1994 Regulations that 'the usefulness of paperwork remains in inverse proportion to the amount'.

6.2 Pre-construction information

This is required on all projects for the purpose of informing designers and contractors of relevant health and safety issues associated with the project. Historical information is initially collected and collated, based on reasonable enquiries made by the client. The client's archive retrieval system is intended to deliver for that very purpose, although it is prudent to appraise the quality and currency of the deliverables. Refer Figure 6.1.

As a process, the pre-construction information stage provides an information source aligned with the needs of the project from concept stage through the incremental design stages, and including the relevant portion of the construction phase itself. The extent of this latter stage would depend on the procurement strategy and the possible timings of specialist work-package appointments, linked to typical 'design and build' arrangements.

On all projects, the author of this document is initially the client, facilitated possibly by the designer as the first member of his professional team. On the multi-contractor project, where a principal designer must be appointed, this duty then passes to the principal designer to deliver the information to other designers and contractors who either have been or will be appointed. Each recipient in turn will feed from this information trail, and as design and construction threads develop, each is duty bound to feed relevant information back into it for the benefit of others. It is the duty of the principal designer to ensure that this happens, notwithstanding the duty of all dutyholders to provide relevant information to others as per the requirements of Regulations 8(5), 8(6) and 9(4). Recipients should get pre-construction information relevant to their role, with no requirement for commonality of content, only for commonality of purpose.

The process is dynamic and therefore the pre-construction information is also part of that dynamic response. This indicates that further pre-construction information, reflective of the unfolding project development, must be provided to relevant dutyholders as appropriate. The provision of this information to the principal designer for distribution greatly facilitates the larger project.

As regards the design process, pre-construction information is a vital starting point for project appreciation and the facilitation of design development thereafter. For the construction process, it is the cardinal information source and the starting point for the drafting of the construction phase plan. Its modus operandi is to provide a focus on the significant health and safety issues that must be accounted for through management controls and health and safety resource compatibility. This project-specific focus is in addition to normal day-to-day management, all of which must be reflected in the tender price submitted.

Failure to identify the salient issues ensures that health and safety considerations remain unaccounted for, leading to a deficient tender submission. Such omissions provide a justifiable argument for additional contractual payment should an issue subsequently manifest itself. The same argument would apply to the late receipt of such information.

Pre-construction information is not a process that delivers exclusively in the period before the construction phase starts but is, rather, a process that delivers before the construction activity itself commences. This process features an elastic and overlapping

---

[1] Chief Inspector of Construction at the launch of the CDM Regulations 1994.

boundary with the construction process and its corresponding construction phase plan authored by either the contractor or principal contractor.

Further guidance is provided in Appendix 2/L153 on the document's purpose and structure, and the level of detail proportionate to the risks involved in the project. The client and principal designer, who are responsible for collecting the information and drafting the document, must decide on relevant content, preferably with input from the principal contractor where possible.

This latter point considers the interface between principal designer and principal contractor for the purposes of constructability appreciation. Early dialogue is the preference, but this is often thwarted by the myriad of procurement routes available to secure projects, coupled with the sacrosanct need for parity of tendering. The enlightened can overcome this through an independent arrangement where needed in order to gain the necessary constructability perspective.

Paragraph 5 of Appendix 2 suggests that

> When pre-construction information is complete, it must include proportionate information about
>
> (a) the project, such as the client brief and key dates of the construction phase;
>
> (b) the planning and management of the project such as the resources and time being allocated to each stage of the project and the arrangement to ensure there is cooperation between dutyholders and the work is coordinated;
>
> (c) the health and safety hazards of the site, including design and construction hazards and how they will be addressed;
>
> (d) any relevant information in an existing health and safety file.

In the sense that pre-construction information is an information process, it is imprudent to consider it as complete at this stage, for the process should continue to capture and deliver information to the dutyholders for as long as it is necessary, which itself is dependent on procurement strategy.

The above sections could beneficially be expanded to include:

section (a) contact details of the client's key personnel; identification of partial handover and sectional completion dates; termination date of the principal designer's appointment;[2]

section (b) form, format and number of copies of the health and safety file; unambiguous delivery date for the health and safety file; welfare arrangements

section (c) any operationally sensitive information (in particular for occupied sites)

section (d) establishment of the currency of the existing health and safety file

all of which could impact on the contractor's/principal contractor's allocation of resources.

6.3 Construction phase plan

This is the most important of the site documents and a critical part of the health and safety managerial control of the construction phase. In a proportionate form it is now required on all construction sites. Its purpose is to articulate the health and safety management detailed control arrangements for all the activities being undertaken on the construction site, and it must remain a dynamic document from the start of the construction phase through to the end of the project, inclusive of work associated with the 'snagging list', which is usually undertaken after project handover.

---

[2] Refer Regulation 12(8).

This document had its origins as the 'Construction Phase Health and Safety Plan' under the 1994 version, was renamed the 'Construction Phase Plan' under the 2007 version and retained the same name under the current version of the Regulations. Whilst there has been a need for minor name changes, its purpose has remained constant, although its usage has now been extended to all construction projects. In respect of this latter point, different models of approach will have to be developed and encouraged to cater for the simple project and to draw a distinction between that and the contextual narrative required for the more complex project, since all projects must now have a construction phase plan.

The document's author is either the single contractor on a single-contractor site or the principal contractor on those sites where it is foreseeable that there will be more than one contractor at any stage during construction. Its importance is endorsed by the fact that it is the one document that the HSE Inspector would choose to see on any site visit. The construction phase plan should be indicative of the proactive management response to the dynamics of health and safety demands of construction activities themselves and the macro requirements of the site as a whole.

The real key to the visualisation of its purpose lies in Regulation 12(4), which requires that

> Throughout the project the principal contractor must ensure that the construction phase plan is appropriately reviewed, updated and revised from time to time so that it continues to be sufficient to ensure that construction work is carried out, so far as is reasonably practicable, without risks to health and safety.

It is the word 'sufficient' that carries the key message, with the implication that it must be sufficient from day one. This accords with the awareness that the most hazardous construction period is the early days of construction site familiarity, for both the starter and the experienced professional. The sufficiency of control documentation from day one is an appreciation that must also stimulate the actions of the client and his advisors.

The construction phase plan lies at the heart of effective management and triggers the client's duty to ensure such arrangements are in place and remain so thereafter.[3] However, the *sufficiency* focus between the client and the contractor/principal contractor allows for much subjectivity and the frustration of the 'drip-feed' response can be avoided through better communication between the parties.

Key method statements, determined critical for the establishment of sufficiency, should be identified in pre-construction information as a basis for consideration by the contractor/principal contractor in the formulation of the draft construction phase plan.

This conveniently distinguishes between the identified front-end site activities and those activities judged as remaining to be fully considered as part of the development of the construction phase plan after construction has started.

As with other aspects of project management the adage 'Planning Longer … Building Quicker' resonates into the more focused form 'Planning Longer … Building Safer and Healthier'. Projects that start off prematurely without the right level of planning can rarely if ever be delivered successfully. This perspective lies at the heart of the site management control process in respect of the preparatory exercise that constitutes the early development of the construction phase plan.

Guidance across the full continuum of construction projects now requiring a construction phase plan is catered for by the simpler approach outlined in HSE document CIS80[4] (see Figure 6.2) and the more comprehensive guidance offered in Appendix 3 of L153.

[3] Regulations 4(1), 4(2) and 4(3).

[4] Construction Phase Plan, CIS80, published by the HSE; see www.hse.gov.uk/construction.

Health and Safety Executive

Construction Phase Plan (CDM 2015)
What you need to know as a busy builder

Under the Construction (Design and Management) Regulations 2015 (CDM 2015) a **construction phase plan** is required for every construction project. This does not need to be complicated.

If you are working for a domestic client, you will be in control of the project if you are the only contractor or the principal contractor.

You will be responsible for:

■ preparing a plan;

■ organising the work; and

■ working together with others to ensure health and safety.

You could be a builder, plumber or other tradesman, doing small-scale routine work such as:

■ installing a kitchen or bathroom;

■ structural alterations, eg chimney breast removal;

■ roofing work, including dormer windows;

■ extension or loft conversion.

A **simple plan** before the work starts is usually enough to show that you have thought about health and safety.

If the job will last longer than 500 person days or 30 working days (with more than 20 people working at the same time) it will need to be notified to HSE and it is likely to be too complex for this simple plan format.

The list of essential points below will help you to **plan** and **organise** the job, and **work together** with others involved to make sure that the work is carried out without risks to health and safety. It will also help you to comply with CDM 2015. You can use the blank template on page 2 to record your plan.

Plan	Working together
Make a note of the key dates, eg: ■ when you'll start and finish; ■ when services will be connected/disconnected; ■ build stages, such as groundwork or fitout. You will need to find out information from the client about the property, eg: ■ where the services and isolation points are; ■ access restriction to the property; ■ if there is any asbestos present.	It may be useful to record the details of anybody else working on the job, including specialist companies and labourers. Explain how you will communicate with others (eg via a daily update), provide information about the job, coordinate your work with theirs and keep them updated of any changes, eg: ■ to site rules; ■ to health and safety information; ■ what you will do if the plan or materials change or if there are any delays; ■ who will be making the key decisions about how the work is to be done.

Organise	
■ Identify the main dangers on site and how you will control them, eg: - the need for scaffolding if working at height; - how structures and excavations will be supported to prevent collapse; - how you will prevent exposure to asbestos and building dust;	- how you will keep the site safe and secure for your client, their family and members of the public. ■ Make sure that there are toilet, washing and rest facilities. ■ Name the person responsible for ensuring the job runs safely. ■ Explain how supervision will be provided.

If you are unsure about how can make your site safer, see www.hse.gov.uk/construction for more information and to download other busy builder sheets. See www.citb.co.uk for a smartphone app *CDM wizard*.

Figure 6.2 Construction phase plan. Contains public sector information published by the Health and Safety Executive and licensed under the Open Government Licence.

			Hazard is present	What controls do you have?
PLAN	Your name/company			
	Name and address of client			
	Contact details of architect or principal designer			
	What is the job? Is there anything the client has made you aware of?			
	Key dates: Start Finish Other			
WORKING TOGETHER	Where are you toilet, washing and rest facilities?			
	Who else is on site – and their contact details?			
	Who will be the principal contractor?			
	How will you keep everyone on site updated during the job?			
ORGANISE	**What are the main dangers on site, eg:**		**Hazard is present**	**What controls do you have?**
	Falls from height ▪ Make sure ladders are in good condition, at the correct angle and secured ▪ Prevent people and materials falling from roofs, gable ends, working platforms and other open edges using guardrails, midrails and toeboards			
	Collapse of excavations ▪ Shore excavations; either cover or barrier excavations to stop people and plant falling in			
	Collapse of structures ▪ Support structures (such as walls, beams, chimney breasts and roofs) with props; ensure props are installed by a competent person			
	Exposure to building dusts ▪ Prevent dust by using wet cutting and vacuum extraction on tools; use a vacuum cleaner rather then sweeping; use a suitable, well-fitting mask			
	Exposure to asbestos ▪ If you suspect that asbestos might be present, don't start work until a demolition/refurbishment survey has been carried out ▪ Make sure everyone on the site is aware of the results			
	Activities or workers requiring supervision ▪ Who will be supervising?			
	Electricity ▪ Turn electricity supply and other services off before drilling walls ▪ Do not use excavators or power tools near suspected buried services			
	Risks to members of the public, the client and others ▪ Keep the site secure to prevent unauthorised access; net scaffolds, use rubbish chutes			
	Other dangers on site			

This guidance is issued by the Health and Safety Executive. Following the guidance is not compulsory, unless specifically stated, and you are free to take other action. But if you do follow the guidance you will normally be doing enough to comply with the law. Health and safety inspectors seek to secure compliance with the law and may refer to this guidance.

Published by the Health and Safety Executive   CIS80   04/15

Figure 6.2 *(Continued)*

The former (of which see below for a sample) provides guidance for the 'busy builder' and is helpful for the smaller operative functioning on the single contractor site who will now have to provide a construction phase plan on such projects. It is imperative that this document is site-specific, and full attention must be given to those issues that come under the heading of 'Other dangers on site'.

The guide has been criticised from some quarters for its simplistic approach but it conveys succinctly the essentials on the small job and embraces the concepts of *proportionality* and *appropriateness*, provided its purpose is duly appreciated.

The note in the last paragraph of the shaded upper box of the extract conveys a salient insight.

The CITB's freely downloadable app 'CITB Wizard' offers a similar facility, but again, attention must be focused on and responsively address all relevant site-specific issues.

Using the guide in paragraph 5/Appendix 3/L153, the following list of topics should be considered when drawing up the plan:

(a) a description of the project such as key dates and details of key members of the project team;

(b) the management of the work including:

    (i) the health and safety aims for the project;

    (ii) the site rules;

    (iii) arrangements to ensure cooperation between project team members and coordination of their work, e.g. regular site meetings;

    (iv) arrangements for involving workers;

    (v) site induction;

    (vi) welfare facilities; and

    (vii) fire and emergency procedures;

(c) the control of any of the specific site risks listed in Schedule 3 where they are relevant to the work involved.

A selective combination of contents from the simple guidance offered by CIS80 to the more comprehensive content of Appendix 3 (L153) provides a vehicle that could satisfy many projects falling between the simple and the more complex.

The robustness of any construction phase plan lies not so much in the document produced but in the review, update and revision process that must shadow the construction phase and deliver amendments, additional information and control tweaks throughout, aided by feedback from the relevant operatives.[5]

Since every document is a static portrayal of a dynamically changing situation it is inevitable that the reality of performance will differ from the predictive visualisation upon which it was originally drafted. Hence, the ongoing review aspect is the most important part of the process and must be considered essential.

All dutyholders contribute to the document, from the client and principal designer, who are charged with providing the initial appreciation via pre-construction information, to the designers who must input residual hazard information, to the contractors via their workplace risk assessments and method statements, all under the overall control of the principal contractor (or contractor on the one-contractor site).

---

[5] Regulation 14: 'Principal contractor's duties to consult and engage with workers.'

This team contribution is ongoing and has no cut-off point during the construction phase, since credible additional information must be passed into the process at all appropriate times.

6.4 Health and safety file

The health and safety file once completed comes into the ownership of the client and is meant to provide an important reference for the completed asset which can be used as a health and safety information source for any future modification, amendment, extension during subsequent maintenance, cleaning, refurbishment, demolition or alteration.

There is a need to distinguish between the numerous administration files that accompany projects and the health and safety file as required by the Regulations. This latter is a statutory requirement and has a legal standing that separates its purpose from other files.

Whilst this statutory document is meant to accompany every construction project on which there is a principal designer (by virtue of there being more than one contractor on site), a challenge must be made to the pragmatic validity of this requirement on all such projects. There is no doubt that the management process of collating and drafting information for the health and safety file must be visible throughout the tenure of the principal designer,[6] but there will be projects which by their very nature will have no relevant content information for the purposes of a health and safety file.

Account must also be taken of the need to cater for the demands of sectional completion and partial handover as characteristics of particular projects. This arrangement will lead to the provision and handover to the client of partially completed health and safety files in the interim periods.

Most projects will indeed deliver a health and safety file, but it is inconceivable that every project with a principal designer will purposefully deliver this document. However, the health and safety file management process must demonstrate evidence of the decision that no such health and safety file was required. Insight and experience need to guide the early discussion between the client, principal designer and principal contractor towards whether the file will be ultimately delivered or not.

Additionally, since this document is a working reference for the client, an initial dialogue is required between the principal designer and client to determine the form and format that best suits the client's management arrangements. Guidance is given in L153[7] on the content, but the form is optional and should be compatible with the client's existing document management systems.

L153 also suggests that there is no need to include information 'that will be of no help when planning future construction work'.[8] This statement aligns with the purpose of the health and safety file, but it continues on to cite both the pre-construction information and the construction phase plan as included within the 'not required' category for the purposes of the health and safety file. This is not a helpful steer, since the focus here should be on any residual hazard factors from either document that would be useful.

This direction should be considered on a project-by-project basis and tempered by the need to consider residual hazard information that could be of use in the health and safety file.

---

[6] Regulation 12(5).

[7] Appendix 4, paragraph 3.

[8] Appendix 4, paragraph 4.

Salient information could well be contained within both documents but not encountered on the majority of projects.[9]

As noted in Regulation 12(8), the early termination of the principal designer's appointment ensures that the final management of the health and safety file legally transfers to the principal contractor. This possibility offers a disconnect in process control and must be identified and notified to the principal contractor prior to his appointment, so that resource compatibility can be factored into his tender price.

The changeover of health and safety file ownership from principal designer to principal contractor needs careful and premeditated planning to facilitate the continuity demanded in document handover, and not least of all to determine the balance between information acquisition and information expectation.

All dutyholders have a proactive role, but there is, by virtue of Regulation 4(3), an overriding requirement for the client to ensure the effectiveness of management arrangements. Some of the above would come within this consideration, with facilitation provided by the client's professional team.

To date, the management and handover of the health and safety file has provided numerous challenges and historically has on occasion resulted in non-delivery, late delivery, inadequate content and mismanagement after handover. Thus, the health and safety file provides an insight into the variable quality of the management process behind it and serves to remind the project team of any dereliction of their statutory duties.

Regulation 12(10) directs that the health and safety file must be passed over to the client at the end of the project, usually by the principal designer but occasionally by the principal contractor. The term 'at the end of the project' is not further defined and therefore introduces some element of ambiguity, in contrast with the comparable 2007 term 'at the end of the construction phase'. This latter term was problematic and often not achieved, partly because of failure to deliver on time and partly because of other elements of managerial process mismanagement. However, it was less ambiguous than the current term.

The term 'at the end of the project' must therefore be determined on a project-by-project basis and could be calculated as the point of handover; final account settlement; end of the defects liability period or at some agreed time in between. The nature of the project itself will provide guidance, but all requisite information should be obtained as and when it ought to be available and before the contributing parties sever links with the project. Managerial astuteness and adequate retention of monies should form part of all projects, particularly the latter, as an incentive for the provision of the health and safety file.

Please note the following in respect of the health and safety file.

General

- Contains information needed to allow future construction work to be carried out healthily and safely.

- Format should be agreed between client and principal designer via early dialogue.

---

[9] Example: Methane is now being dawn off landfill sites and via ring main connectors transformed into electricity and fed into the national grid. Transformer design is based on a predicted draw-off from the guesstimate of reservoir capacity. Off-loading craneage areas are duly designed, engineered and prepared, frequently on poor sub-strata, to receive and install the specified transformers. In due course the methane draw-off could exceed or disappoint early predictions and existing transformers would subsequently need to be uprated or reduced in capacity. Relevant pre-construction information and construction phase plan methodology could benefit the content of the corresponding health and safety file.

- Not a document for day-to-day maintenance and therefore distinct from the O&M[10] manuals.

- Focused contributions by client, designers, principal designer, contractors[11] and principal contractor.

- Associated with all projects on which there is principal designer. (**Note:** see previous comment on this point).

- Future ownership must be considered, for there may be more than one health and safety file per project.[12]

Client: Regulation 4(7)

- Needs early consideration of the number of copies eventually required and their form and format.

- Must keep possession after handover.

- Must make it available to those persons who may need it to comply with their statutory duties.

- 'Duty of care' to maintain its currency after handover.

- Must hand it over to any new owner together with a letter explaining its nature and purpose.

- Leaseholders etc. will require relevant abstracts from the health and safety file.

- An existing (current) health and safety file forms the basis of information provision for the pre-construction information process of any future related project.

Principal Designer: Regulations 12(5), 12(6), 12(8) and 12(10)

- Initiates early dialogue with the client to determine the form and format of the health and safety file.

- Must ensure that management process for preparation and collation of the document is demonstrably visible from the pre-construction phase and throughout the subsequent construction stages.

- Does not have to check its accuracy but must focus on expected content.

- Must collect residual hazard information from the design process via the designers, as and when available.

- Liaises with the principal contractor regarding the coordination of inputs from the various contractors/sub-contractors.

- Should ensure relevant information is received and dates established for receipt of such information.

- Hands file over to the client at the end of the project or alternatively to the principal contractor if the principal designer's commission is terminated before the end of the project.

- Should ensure that partial and sectional completions are accompanied by appropriate partially completed versions of the health and safety file.

---

[10] Operation and Maintenance.

[11] Contractors' inputs would be via collation by the principal contractor.

[12] Example: Speculative housing development with the need for a health and safety file per house as well as a health and safety file for the local authority for the adoptable 'roads and sewers'.

Designers: Regulation 9(3)

- Promptly provide residual hazard information to the principal designer for inclusion in the health and safety file.

Contractors: Regulation 8(6)

- Promptly provide the principal contractor with relevant information for inclusion in the health and safety file.

Principal Contractor: Regulation 13(3)

- Identify for each contractor their required input and date for delivery of relevant information.

- Ensure relevant information is promptly passed over to the principal designer.

Note: the duties arising out of Regulation 9(4): Duties of designers,[13] ensure that regardless of the existence of a health and safety file there will always be the need for the provision of information. This could be a particular point of focus on the smaller project where there may not be a principal designer and the construction work being undertaken, however limited, could nevertheless lead to an amendment/ update/modification to an existing health and safety file.

---

[13] Regulation 9(4): 'A designer must take all reasonable steps to provide, with the design, sufficient information about the design, construction or maintenance of the structure, to adequately assist the client, other designers and contractors to comply with their duties under these Regulations.'

7 Questions

7.1 Questionnaire 1

No.	DESCRIPTION	True	False
	The CDM Regulations 2015: Questionnaire 1		
1	These Regulations apply only to notifiable construction projects.		
2	These Regulations do not apply to domestic construction projects unless they are notifiable.		
3	There must be a principal contractor on every construction project.		
4	Domestic client projects must have a principal contractor.		
5	There must be a principal designer on every construction project.		
6	If there is a principal contractor then there must be a principal designer.		
7	If there is a principal designer then there must be a principal contractor.		
8	The 'lead designer' will automatically become the principal designer.		
9	A single designer could become the principal designer.		
10	A single contractor on a project could become the principal contractor.		
11	Pre-construction information is required on all projects.		
12	Notification to the HSE must be made by the principal designer.		
13	Notification to the HSE must be made before significant detailed design begins.		
14	Notification to the HSE is the trigger point for the appointment of the principal designer.		
15	The notification to the HSE must be on display in the site canteen.		
16	A construction phase plan is required only on notifiable projects.		
17	Once the construction phase plan is being prepared then the construction phase can start.		
18	A health and safety file is required on all projects.		
19	The health and safety file must be handed over at the end of the construction phase.		
20	The health and safety file is initially prepared by the principal contractor.		

CDM Regulations 2015 Procedures Manual, Fourth Edition. Stuart D. Summerhayes.
© 2016 John Wiley & Sons, Ltd. Published 2016 by John Wiley & Sons, Ltd.

7.2 Questionnaire 2

	The CDM Regulations 2015: Questionnaire 2		
No.	**DESCRIPTION**	**True**	**False**
1	The client has ONLY to appoint a principal designer and principal contractor on notifiable projects.		
2	The principal designer MUST appoint a principal contractor in writing.		
3	There only needs to be a principal contractor when there is MORE THAN ONE contractor working on a construction project.		
4	The client cannot function as the principal contractor.		
5	The client can function as the principal designer.		
6	The principal designer has no involvement with the drafting of the construction phase plan.		
7	The construction phase plan MUST be drawn up as soon as practicable after the setting up of the construction site.		
8	There MUST be a principal designer and principal contractor on all notifiable projects.		
9	The principal designer MUST ensure that all designers comply with their duties under Regulation 9.		
10	The author of the construction phase plan is the client.		
11	Estimating the time period for completion of the construction project or its relevant stages remains the SOLE responsibility of the contractor.		
12	The client MUST ensure welfare facilities are adequate before construction work begins.		
13	All parties working within the construction project must be competent.		
14	Every contractor MUST comply with relevant directions given by the principal designer.		
15	The client MUST ensure that the construction phase plan and the health and safety file are reviewed, revised and updated throughout the project.		
16	The client would NEVER have a dutyholder role under these Regulations.		
17	The principal contractor has an absolute duty to consult with workers on health and safety project matters, in good time, throughout the project.		
18	There would be NO health and safety file on a domestic client project.		
19	An input to the health and safety file is ONLY required on a notifiable project.		
20	The health and safety file MUST be handed over to the client by the principal contractor.		

8

Assignments

8.1 Assignment 1

ASSIGNMENT ONE

Please comment on the highlighted points raised by circling your answer in the right-hand column.

The Regional Business Manager of BC Holdings Ltd has appointed PH Mechanical Services Ltd to design and supply four new 50 tonne aggregate bins as part of an expansion/remediation programme to the existing ready mixed concrete plant.

The work entails site clearance and the removal of obsolete electricity poles (two-week duration); part demolition of an obsolete retaining wall and foundations (three-weeks duration); and the construction of new foundations and the erection with in-situ welding of the new loading bins(4 weeks).

This latter work, which also includes electrical supply etc., will be done on site by the company's direct labour force whilst the demolition and site clearance has been sub-let to XYZ Construction Services. It is anticipated that there will be a one-week overlap with part demolition and new foundation construction taking place at the same time.

The business manager has sanctioned the **site clearance work, since this is in advance of the main contract proper**[1] and does not come under the definition of **construction of a structure**[2]. Therefore a less formal approach can be adopted.	1. CORRECT/INCORRECT 2. TRUE/FALSE
The business manager has appointed a project manager **as required**[3] by the CDM Regulations 2015, from within his team.	3. TRUE/FALSE
As a result of his understanding of the new regulations a notification has already been sent off **by the project manager**[4], in readiness for the demolition phase etc., and is **on display in the plant operational office**[5].	4. CORRECT/INCORRECT 5. CORRECT/INCORRECT
In response to a query he explains that the notification is always required on projects that are **either greater than 30 days of construction time**[6] or **more than £50,000 in tender value**[7].	6. CORRECT/INCORRECT 7. CORRECT/INCORRECT
BC Holdings Ltd has **provided only a copy of the site rules and a copy of the notification**[8] to PH Mechanical Services Ltd, who are responsible for the demolition, as a contract prime cost sum. Prior to a start on site XYZ Construction Services has provided the necessary method statements and, **on the assumption that they are accepted**[9], intends to start work Monday next.	8. CORRECT/INCORRECT 9. SATISFACTORY/UNSATISFACTORY
The start is imminent and BC Holdings Ltd has indicated that they are not going to request any further information in keeping with the **less bureaucratic requirements of the new regulations**[10].	10. ACCCEPTABLE/UNACCEPTABLE

(Continued)

CDM Regulations 2015 Procedures Manual, Fourth Edition. Stuart D. Summerhayes.
© 2016 John Wiley & Sons, Ltd. Published 2016 by John Wiley & Sons, Ltd.

The majority of the remaining work is to be done under the management of BC Holdings Ltd's service manager and therefore **no further appointments have to be made**[11].	**11. CORRECT/INCORRECT**
The company prides itself on the rigour of its approved subcontractor list, which **ensures that effective management arrangements**[12] are implemented by all parties with which it enters into contract. This makes life easier and releases BC Holdings Ltd from **ongoing monitoring of management arrangements**[13].	**12. SATISFACTORY/UNSATISFACTORY** **13. SATISFACTORY/UNSATISFACTORY**
Finally, relevant information will be handed over to the business manager by XYZ Construction Services **via the project manager**[14] at the **end of the construction phase**[15] without the **need for a health and safety file**[16] to be delivered by PH Mechanical Services Ltd, **who are only functioning as project designer**[17].	**14. SATISFACTORY/UNSATISFACTORY** **15. SATISFACTORY/UNSATISFACTORY** **16. SATISFACTORY/UNSATISFACTORY** **17. CORRECT/INCORRECT**
S D Summerhayes/Nov. 2015	

8.2 Assignment 2

ASSIGNMENT TWO: DOCUMENTATION

Please comment on the highlighted points raised by circling your answer in the right-hand column.

A new two-storey office extension is being undertaken for Excelsior Products Ltd at The Parkhead Retail Complex, with a scheduled completion six months from now. The project is under the control of Excelsior's Project Manager, with the bulk of the construction work being done by Construction Ltd using its directly employed workforce, supplemented by some specialist fit-out undertaken by Integrated Mechanical Solutions, who arrived on site two weeks ago. The design of the project is in the hands of Excelsior Products Ltd in-house design team based in Dartford, under the remit of their design manager.

An independent project, won by AB Specialists Ltd, has also commenced within the retail complex, involving the construction of a new one-storey IT building and the demolition of the existing facility. Completion is programmed for three months time and a local demolition contractor is now involved in demolition and site clearance.

A.	Excelsior Products has **developed an initial Construction Phase Plan**[1], which has been passed to their design manager for further development **but is still awaiting his attention**[2].	1. Satisfactory/unsatisfactory 2. Satisfactory/unsatisfactory
B.	This draft version has been **based on a site walk-over made by the design team and some residual hazard information arising out of the design process**[3]. The Client is pleased that **all compliance procedures have been followed**[4] to date.	3. Satisfactory/unsatisfactory 4. Correct/incorrect
C.	**Now that Integrated Mechanical Solutions are on site, Construction Ltd has taken up the role of Principal Contractor**[5] and Excelsior Products Ltd has asked them for **their Construction Phase Plan**[6].	5. Satisfactory/unsatisfactory 6. Satisfactory/unsatisfactory
D.	The first **notification was sent off**[7] as part of the design process by the design manager and now that the second contractor is on site, **an amended notification has been sent to the HSE**[8], which is **displayed in Construction Ltd's welfare facility**[9].	7. Correct/incorrect 8. Satisfactory/unsatisfactory 9. Satisfactory/unsatisfactory
E.	Since there is only one designer involved **no Principal Designer has been appointed**[10], so the **health and safety file is being drafted by the Principal Contractor**[11].	10. Correct/incorrect 11. Correct/incorrect
F.	It transpires that through the course of a number of site progress meetings it is obvious that the **Client is uncertain about his duties**[12] and has asked **someone to explain them to him**[13].	12. Satisfactory/unsatisfactory 13. Satisfactory/unsatisfactory
G.	The IT building project is **using the same Construction Phase Plan**[14] as the office extension project to reduce unnecessary paperwork on the basis that **it hasn't changed since it was originally drafted**[15]. No principal contractor has been appointed, since **AB Specialists Ltd**[16] are doing the bulk of the work.	14. Correct/incorrect 15. Satisfactory/unsatisfactory 16. Satisfactory/unsatisfactory
H.	The two projects partly overlap in terms of site boundaries, although there is **little contact between the sets of contractors**[17] on the basis that everyone is experienced and knows what they are doing.	17. Satisfactory/unsatisfactory
I.	Construction Ltd is ensuring that its workforce benefit **solely from the retail complex's own site induction**[18], before starting work, whilst on the IT project site it appears that **no site induction process has ever taken place**[19].	18. Satisfactory/unsatisfactory 19. Satisfactory/unsatisfactory
J.	The guidance **provided by the Design Manager**[20] for the content of the health and safety file appears to demand the inclusion of: **F10 Notification**[21]; **Construction Phase Plan**[22]; **Retail Manager's Site Rules**[23] and **records of all site accidents**[24].	20. Correct/incorrect 21. Satisfactory/unsatisfactory 22. Satisfactory/unsatisfactory 23. Satisfactory/unsatisfactory 24. Satisfactory/unsatisfactory

S D Summerhayes/Nov. 2015

Commentaries

9.1 Commentary on Questionnaire 1

No.	DESCRIPTION	True	False
	The CDM Regulations 2015: Questionnaire 1		
1	These Regulations apply only for notifiable construction projects. **These Regulations apply to all projects defined as construction projects regardless of the notification process.**		✓
2	These Regulations do not apply to domestic client construction projects unless they are notifiable. **Domestic client projects are subject to the full ramifications of the Regulations. Client duties, however, represent a particular case, (Regulation 7), with such client duties being placed on other dutyholders.**		✓
3	There must be a principal contractor on every construction project. **Only if it is foreseeable that there will be more than one contractor on the project at any time. Regulation 5(1)(a).**		✓
4	Domestic client projects must have a principal contractor. **Only if it is foreseeable that there will be more than one contractor on the project at any time. Regulation 5(1)(a).**		✓
5	There must be a principal designer on every construction project **Only if it is foreseeable that there will be more than one contractor on the project at any time. Regulation 5(1)(a).**		✓
6	If there is a principal contractor then there must be a principal designer. **As per Regulation 5(1)(b).**	✓	
7	If there is a principal designer then there must be a principal contractor. **Regulation 5(1)(a) and 5(1)(b).**	✓	
8	The 'lead designer' will automatically become the principal designer. **There is no reference to the 'lead designer' anywhere in the current Regulations. (Whilst it was not mentioned as an appointment in the previous version of the Regulations, the previous ACoP (L144) did champion such an appointment.)**		✓
9	A single designer could become the principal designer. **Because of the wording of Regulation 5(1)(a), which is dependent only on there being more than one contractor on site at any time.**	✓	
10	A single contractor on a project could become the principal contractor. **False, since Regulation 5(1)(a) refers to more than one contractor. (Since this appointment depends on the foreseeability of there being another contractor, there could be times when the only contractor on site is indeed the principal contractor, i.e. it is an appointment in readiness, made before the start of the construction phase. Regulation 5(2)).**		✓

(Continued)

CDM Regulations 2015 Procedures Manual, Fourth Edition. Stuart D. Summerhayes.
 © 2016 John Wiley & Sons, Ltd. Published 2016 by John Wiley & Sons, Ltd.

The CDM Regulations 2015: Questionnaire 1			
No.	DESCRIPTION	True	False
11	Pre-construction information is required on all projects. **Regulation 4(1)(4) and Regulation 14(6).**	✔	
12	Notification to the HSE must be made by the principal designer. **Regulation 6(2), but this does not translate into the client having to do it in a hands-on way. It could be facilitated by the design team or any other party but it remains the client's duty to ensure that this happens.**		✔
13	Notification to the HSE must be made before significant detailed design begins. **Regulation 6(2) refers to notification being made to the Executive as soon as possible, before the construction phase begins, and makes no reference to the term as such. The term 'significant detailed design' has no relevance in this current version of the Regulations.**		✔
14	Notification to the HSE is the trigger point for the appointment of the principal designer. **Notification and appointments are totally divorced. Regulation 5 and Regulation 7.**		✔
15	The notification to the HSE must be on display in the site canteen. **Display must be made in the construction site office and in some cases this building could also house the site canteen, but the wording speaks of the construction site office. Regulation 6(3)(b).**		✔
16	A construction phase plan is required only on notifiable projects. **All projects regardless of project cost or duration must be accompanied by a construction phase plan (appropriate and proportional). Regulation 15(5) and paragraph 42/L153.**		✔
17	Once the construction phase plan is being prepared then the construction phase can start. **Guidance on the requirement here is contained in Regulation 12(4), which requires that this document 'continues to be sufficient'. Regulations 4(1), 4(3) and 15(5) also support this.**		✔
18	A health and safety file is required on all projects. **It is dependent on there being a principal designer, who is the author of such a document. Regulations 12(5) and 12(6).**		✔
19	The health and safety file must be handed over at the end of the construction phase. **The wording of Regulation 12(10) clearly identifies the handover point as 'at the end of the project'. This needs to be defined on a project-by-project basis.**		✔
20	The health and safety file is initially prepared by the principal contractor. **It is the principal designer who initiates the health and safety file (Regulation 12(5)), and who would usually hand it over unless his appointment concludes before the end of the project. The duty to complete and hand over would then pass to the principal contractor (Regulation 12(8)).**		✔

9.2 Commentary on Questionnaire 2

	The CDM Regulations 2015: Questionnaire 2		
No.	**DESCRIPTION**	**True**	**False**
1	The client has to appoint a principal designer and principal contractor ONLY on notifiable projects. **The appointment and notification processes are entirely independent of one another. Regulations 5(1) and 7.**		✓
2	The principal designer MUST appoint a principal contractor in writing. **Such an appointment must be made by the client (in writing). Regulation 5(1)(b).**		✓
3	There only needs to be a principal contractor when there is MORE THAN ONE contractor working on a construction project. **The exact wording is that a principal contractor needs to be appointed 'if it is reasonably foreseeable that more than one contractor will be working on a project at any time'. Regulation 5(1).**	✓	
4	The client cannot function as the principal contractor. **Provided he has the skills, knowledge and experience, and, if ... an organisation, the organising capability, necessary to fulfil the role. Regulation 8(1). It cannot be based purely on convenience!**		✓
5	The client can function as the principal designer. **Provided he has 'the skills, knowledge and experience and, if ... an organisation, the organising capability, necessary to fulfil the role'. Regulation 8(1). It cannot be based purely on convenience!**	✓	
6	The principal designer has no involvement with the drafting of the construction phase plan. **Regulation 11(7) requires that there be liaison between principal designer and principal contractor for the purpose of the planning, management and monitoring of the contraction phase plan.**		✓
7	The construction phase plan MUST be drawn up as soon as practicable after the setting up of the construction site. **Regulation 12(1) requires that the initial drafting is done 'during the pre-construction phase and before setting up a construction site'.**		✓
8	There MUST be a principal designer and principal contractor on all notifiable projects. **The criterion for appointment is dependent only on the foreseeability of there being more than one contractor at any time during the project. Regulation 5(1).**		✓
9	The principal designer MUST ensure that all designers comply with their duties under Regulation 9. **As per Regulation 11(4).**	✓	
10	The author of the construction phase plan is the client. **It is either the contractor Regulation 15(5) or the principal contractor as per Regulations 12(1) and 12(4).**		✓
11	Estimating the time period to complete the construction project or its relevant stages remains the SOLE responsibility of the contractor. **Regulations 11(2)(b) and 13(1) place this duty on the principal designer and principal contractor.**		✓
12	The client MUST ensure welfare facilities are adequate before construction work begins. **As per Regulation 4(2)(b), noting that it is the client's duty to ensure that they are provided, but not his duty to provide them.**	✓	

(Continued)

9 Commentaries

The CDM Regulations 2015: Questionnaire 2			
No.	**DESCRIPTION**	**True**	**False**
13	All parties working within the construction project must be competent. **Regulation 8(1) makes reference to the dutyholders having the necessary skills, knowledge and experience, together with the operational capability, if they are an organisation. This is pragmatically directed at the team's competence. A better focus is given in Regulation 15(7), which mentions every employee having 'or [being] in the process of obtaining, the necessary skills, knowledge, training and experience'. So it is the team's competence that is judged, otherwise there would be no route for new inexperienced members of the team to pursue.**		✓
14	Every contractor MUST comply with relevant directions given by the principal designer. **Regulation 15(3)(a) says just this, provided there is more than one contractor on site. Prudence and best practice, nonetheless, must direct any such approach via the principal contractor, who is in control of the construction site and all things relevant to its management.**	✓	
15	The client MUST ensure that the construction phase plan and the health and safety file are reviewed, revised and updated throughout the project. **Regulation 4(3), linked to Regulations 12(4) and 12(6), confirms this need, since these are primary management duties falling to the principal contractor and principal designer respectively.**	✓	
16	The client would NEVER have a dutyholder role under these Regulations. **He has an implicit duty as outlined in Regulation 4 and other duties should he also choose to function as designer, principal designer, contractor and/or principal contractor. Duties could also default to him under Regulations 5(3) and 5(4).**		✓
17	The principal contractor has an absolute duty to consult with workers on health and safety project matters, in good time, throughout the project. **As per Regulation 14(b).**	✓	
18	There would be NO health and safety file on a domestic client project. **If there is a principal designer then there should be a health and safety file. Regulation 12(5).**		✓
19	An input to the health and safety file is ONLY required on a notifiable project. **As per Regulation 12(5) regarding the appointment of a principal designer, which is not linked to the notification process and also ongoing designer duties under Regulation 9(4), which could affect an existing health and safety file.**		✓
20	The health and safety file MUST be handed over to the client by the principal contractor. **Regulation 12(10) states that this must be done by the principal designer, or by the principal contractor where the principal designer's appointment has concluded.**		✓

9.3 Commentary on Assignment 1

Please comment on the highlighted points raised by circling your answer in the right-hand column.

The Regional Business Manager of BC Holdings Ltd has appointed PH Mechanical Services Ltd to design and supply four new 50 tonne aggregate bins as part of an expansion/remediation programme to the existing ready mixed concrete plant.

The work entails site clearance and the removal of obsolete electricity poles (two-week duration); part demolition of an obsolete retaining wall and foundations (three-weeks duration) and the construction of new foundations and the erection with in-situ welding of the new loading bins (4 weeks).

This latter work, which also includes electrical supply etc., will be done on site by the company's direct labour force whilst the demolition and site clearance has been sub-let to XYZ Construction Services. It is anticipated that there will be a one-week overlap with part demolition and new foundation construction taking place at the same time.

A.	The business manager has sanctioned the site clearance work, since this is in advance of the main contract proper[1] and does not come under the definition of construction of a structure[2]. Therefore a less formal approach can be adopted.	1. CORRECT/**INCORRECT** 2. TRUE/**FALSE**

1. Regulation 2 defines 'clearance work' as part of the definition of construction and therefore indicative that the project has started.
2. Strictly speaking anything that comes under the Regulation 2 definition of 'construction of a structure' is subject to the CDM Regulations 2015. This is the case here.

B.	The business manager has appointed a project manager as required[3] by the CDM Regulations 2015, from within his team.	3. TRUE/**FALSE**

3. Nowhere do the Regulations require the appointment of a project manager. Only two appointments have to be made by the client under the CDM Regulations 2015. These are the appointments of the principal designer and the principal contractor as required by Regulation 5. All other appointments are contractual.

C.	As a result of his understanding of the new Regulations a notification has already been sent off by the project manager[4], in readiness for the demolition phase etc., and is on display in the plant operational office[5].	4. CORRECT/**INCORRECT** 5. CORRECT/**INCORRECT**

4. Regulation 6(1) requires the client to give notice to the HSE if the criteria for notification has been met (possibly unlikely in this case unless there are more than 20 workers working simultaneously on the project at any point). The project manager could send it off, but it remains the client's duty to ensure it is sent.
5. Should be displayed in the construction site office. Regulation 6(3).

D.	In response to a query he explains that the notification is always required on projects that are either greater than 30 days of construction time[6] or more than £50,000 in tender value[7].	6. CORRECT/**INCORRECT** 7. CORRECT/**INCORRECT**

6 & 7. Regulation 6(1)(a) and 6(1)(b) provide the only criteria for notification in this case.

E.	BC Holdings Ltd has provided only a copy of the site rules and a copy of the notification[8] to PH Mechanical Services Ltd, who are responsible for the demolition, as a contract prime cost sum. Prior to a start on site XYZ Construction Services has provided the necessary method statements and, on the assumption that they are accepted[9], intends to start work Monday next.	8. CORRECT/**INCORRECT** 9. SATISFACTORY/**UNSATISFACTORY**

8. This is pre-construction information and would not be adequate as described. Refer L153.
9. This would not represent acceptable control, since this represents the construction phase plan, which must be suitable before construction can start.

(Continued)

Commentary on Assignment 1

F. The start is imminent and BC Holdings Ltd has indicated that they are not going to request any further information in keeping with the less bureaucratic requirements of the new Regulations[10].

10. ACCCEPTABLE/**UNACCEPTABLE**

10. What has been presented above would not be deemed adequate and therefore the construction phase plan is deficient in content.

G. The majority of the remaining work is to be done under the management of BC Holdings Ltd's service manager and therefore no further appointments have to be made[11].

11. CORRECT/**INCORRECT**

11. There are two contractors on site and therefore under Regulation 5(1), a principal designer and principal contractor should have been appointed by the client in writing, or if not such duties will default back onto the client. Regulation 5(3) and 5(4).

H. The company prides itself on the rigour of its approved subcontractor list, which ensures that effective management arrangements[12] are implemented by all parties with which it enters into contract. This makes life easier and releases BC Holdings Ltd from ongoing monitoring of management arrangements[13].

12. SATISFACTORY/**UNSATISFACTORY**
13. SATISFACTORY/**UNSATISFACTORY**

12. The approved subcontractor list does not itself endorse the implementation or effectiveness of management arrangements. These must be appraised separately.
13. Ongoing monitoring of the effectiveness of management arrangements remains a duty on the client under Regulation (3).

I. Finally, relevant information will be handed over to the business manager by XYZ Construction Services via the project manager[14] at the end of the construction phase[15] without the need for a health and safety file[16] to be delivered by PH Mechanical Services Ltd, who are only functioning as project designer[17].

14. SATISFACTORY/**UNSATISFACTORY**
15. SATISFACTORY/**UNSATISFACTORY**
16. SATISFACTORY/**UNSATISFACTORY**
17. CORRECT/**INCORRECT**

14. This is information that should go into the health and safety file via the principal contractor to the principal designer.
15. Health and safety file to be handed over at the end of the project. Regulation 12(10).
16. Since there should be a principal designer, there must be a health and safety file. Regulation 12(5) and 12(6).
17. PH Mechanical Services must be functioning as the principal designer, since there are two contractors on site. Regulation 5(1)(a), or the client by default. Regulation 5(3).

9.4   Commentary on Assignment 2

| Commentary on Assignment 2 |

Please comment on the highlighted points raised by circling your answer in the right-hand column.

A new two-storey office extension is being undertaken for Excelsior Products Ltd at The Parkhead Retail Complex, with a scheduled completion six months from now. The project is under the control of Excelsior's Project Manager, with the bulk of the construction work being done by Construction Ltd using its directly employed workforce, supplemented by some specialist fit-out undertaken by Integrated Mechanical Solutions, who arrived on site two weeks ago. The design of the project is in the hands of Excelsior Products Ltd in-house design team based in Dartford, under the remit of their design manager.

An independent project, won by AB Specialists Ltd, has also commenced within the retail complex, involving the construction of a new one-storey IT building and the demolition of the existing facility. Completion is programmed for three months time and a local demolition contractor is now involved in demolition and site clearance.

A.   Excelsior Products has developed an initial Construction Phase Plan[1], which has been passed to their design manager for further development but is still awaiting his attention[2].

1. Satisfactory/**unsatisfactory**
2. Satisfactory/**unsatisfactory**

   1. The construction phase plan is meant to be developed by either the contractor or principal contractor, not the client. Regulations 12(1) and 15(5).
   2. As above.

B.   This draft version has been based on a site walk-over made by the design team and some residual hazard information arising out of the design process[3]. The Client is pleased that all compliance procedures have been followed[4] to date.

3. Satisfactory/**unsatisfactory**
4. Correct/**incorrect**

   3. Inadequate since the construction phase plan should be based on pre-construction information. What is described does not constitute pre-construction information ... Regulation 12(3).
   4. As above, which is indicative that all compliance procedures have not been followed.

C.   Now that Integrated Mechanical Solutions are on site, Construction Ltd has taken up the role of Principal Contractor[5] and Excelsior Products Ltd has asked them for their Construction Phase Plan[6].

5. Satisfactory/**unsatisfactory**
6. Satisfactory/**unsatisfactory**

   5. The role of the principal contractor commences at the start of the construction phase as per Regulation 12(1), regardless of when the second contractor arrives on site.
   6. The construction phase plan should be sufficient from day one of the construction phase, with a duty on the principal contractor (Regulation 12(4)), and on the client (Regulation 4(2)).

D.   The first notification was sent off[7] as part of the design process by the design manager and now that the second contractor is on site an amended notification has been sent to the HSE[8], which is displayed in Construction Ltd's welfare facility[9].

7. Correct/**incorrect**
8. Satisfactory/**unsatisfactory**
9. Satisfactory/**unsatisfactory**

   7. Since Regulation 6(2) requires notification to be given before the construction phase begins, it is not the timing but the reference to the first notification that is perhaps unusual, suggesting a connection with the procedures followed under the 2007 Regulations, and therefore an outdated response. Not an issue in itself but more a lack of appreciation of the changes under the 2015 Regulations.
   8. A matter of subjectivity, but no real need for an amended notification in respect of the second contractor, since this doesn't itself signify a significant alteration to information already provided.
   9. Notification should be displayed in the construction site office. Regulation 6(3).

E.   Since there is only one designer involved no Principal Designer has been appointed[10], so the health and safety file is being drafted by the Principal Contractor[11].

10. Correct/**incorrect**
11. Correct/**incorrect**

   10. The appointment of a principal designer is dependent only on there being more than one contractor on site at any time ... Regulation 5(1)(a).
   11. The health and safety file is initially drafted by the principal designer. Regulation 12(5).

(Continued)

	Commentary on Assignment 2

F.	It transpires that through the course of a number of site progress meetings it is obvious that the Client is uncertain about his duties[12] and has asked someone to explain them to him[13].	12. Satisfactory/**unsatisfactory** 13. Satisfactory/**unsatisfactory**

12. This possibility should have been addressed by all designers and contractors, by virtue of Regulations 9(1) and 15(1) respectively, before any of them embarked on their work in the project.
13. Beyond the implications above it is to the benefit of the project that the client's ability to understand his duties is demonstrated by his discharge of those duties. This discharge should be shadowed by the client's professional advisors and action taken to reinforce the client's understanding if such duties are not fully appreciated and demonstrated by him. There is a distinction here between what the law says and the best practice approach which requires a higher standard of delivery.

G.	The IT Building project is using the same Construction Phase Plan[14] as the office extension project to reduce unnecessary paperwork on the basis that it hasn't changed since it was originally drafted[15]. No principal contractor has been appointed, since AB Specialists Ltd[16] are doing the bulk of the work.	14. Correct/**incorrect** 15. Satisfactory/**unsatisfactory** 16. Satisfactory/**unsatisfactory**

14. Each construction phase plan is meant to be project specific. Regulation 12(2).
15. Regulation 12(4) requires the construction phase plan to be 'reviewed, updated and revised' throughout the project, hence it is a dynamic document.
16. AB Specialists are doing the bulk of the work, but there is still more than one contractor on site. Therefore a principal designer and principal contractor must be appointed by the client, or by default the duties will fall to the client to discharge. Regulations 5(1), 5(3) and 5(4).

H.	The two projects partly overlap in terms of site boundaries, although there is little contact between the sets of contractors[17] on the basis that everyone is experienced and knows what they are doing.	17. Satisfactory/**unsatisfactory**

17. Regulation 8(4) requires cooperation with others at the same or adjoining construction sites. This has obviously not happened.

I.	Construction Ltd is ensuring that its workforce benefit solely; from the retail complex's own site induction[18], before starting work, whilst on the IT project site it appears that no site induction process has ever taken place[19].	18. Satisfactory/**unsatisfactory** 19. Satisfactory/**unsatisfactory**

18. Regulation 13(1)(4) requires the principal contractor to ensure a suitable site induction is provided. This must relate to the construction project specifics and would be additional to the client's own site induction.
19. As above.

J.	The guidance provided by the Design Manager[20] for the content of the health and safety file appears to demand the inclusion of: F10 Notification[21]; Construction Phase Plan[22]; Retail Manager's Site Rules[23] and records of all site accidents[24].	20. Correct/**incorrect** 21. Satisfactory/**unsatisfactory** 22. Satisfactory/**unsatisfactory** 23. Satisfactory/**unsatisfactory** 24. Satisfactory/**unsatisfactory**

20. Guidance on the content of the health and safety file should have been provided by the principal designer in pre-construction information, since he is managing the health and safety file process. Regulation 12(5).
21. See L153. F10 notification not required.
22. Identify and include any relevant residual hazard information.
23. Not relevant for the purposes of the health and safety file.
24. Not relevant for the purposes of the health and safety file.

Appendices

A.1 Dutyholder Summary Sheets

CDM Regulations 2015 Procedures Manual, Fourth Edition. Stuart D. Summerhayes.
© 2016 John Wiley & Sons, Ltd. Published 2016 by John Wiley & Sons, Ltd.

Table A.1 Client summary CDM 2015

SUMMARY OF DUTIES UNDER THE CDM REGULATIONS 2015

Duty holder	Pre-construction		Construction phase	
Client	**For all projects:**		**For all projects:**	
	1. Ensure all appointees have the skills, knowledge experience and operational capabilities to satisfactorily fulfil their role.	8(3)	1. Ensure all appointees have the skills, knowledge experience and operational capabilities to satisfactorily fulfil their role.	8(3)
	2. Make suitable arrangements for managing the project.	4(1)	2. Make suitable arrangements for managing the project.	4(1)
	3. Ensure management arrangements remain effective throughout the project.	4(3)	3. Ensure management arrangements remain effective throughout the project.	4(3)
	4. Provide pre-construction information.	4(4)	4. Provide pre-construction information.	4(4)
	5. Ensure a construction phase plan is drawn up or arrangements made for it to be drawn up by the contractor.	4(5)(a)	5. Ensure the health and safety file is kept available for inspection by those who need it.	4(5)(b)
	6. Ensure the health and safety file is kept available for inspection by those who need it.	4(5)(b)		
	7. Must cooperate with others at the same or adjoining site.	8(4)		
	8. Provide relevant information promptly and in a comprehensible form.	8(6)		
	9. Ensure design done outside GB complies with Reg. 9 if not commissioned within GB.	10		
	For projects with more than one contractor:		**For projects with more than one contractor:**	
	1. Appoint principal designer and principal contractor in writing as soon as possible.	5(1)*	1. Take reasonable steps to ensure principal designer complies with duties under Regulations 11 and 12.	4(6)(a)
	2. Ensure a construction phase plan is drawn up or arrangements made for it to be drawn up by principal contractor.	4(5)(a)	2. Take reasonable steps to ensure principal contractor complies with duties under Regulations 12 to 14.	4(6)(b)
	3. Take reasonable steps to ensure principal designer complies with duties under Regulations 11 and 12.	4(6)(a)	3. Ensure principal designer prepares and revises the health and safety file.	4(5)(b)
	4. Takes reasonable steps to ensure principal contractor complies with duties under Regulations 12 to 14.	4(6)(b)		
	5. Must ensure principal designer prepares and revises the health and safety file.	5(3) & 5(4)		
	NOTE: failure to appoint a principal designer and/or principal contractor renders the client responsible for each of the duties.			
	For notifiable projects:		**For notifiable projects:**	
	1. Notify relevant authority as soon as possible.	6(2)	1. Ensure the notification is displayed in the construction site office.	6(3)

*Refer footnote

*Note: Reg. 7: Where asset changes ownership, existing client to hand over the health and safety file and explain the nature and purpose of the file to the incoming owner.

Table A.2 Domestic client summary CDM 2015

SUMMARY OF DUTIES UNDER THE CDM REGULATIONS 2015

Duty holder	Pre-construction		START OF CONSTRUCTION	Construction phase	END OF CONSTRUCTION
Domestic client	**For single contractor projects:**			Duties fall to:	
	1. Client duties to be undertaken by the contractor, or	7(1)(a)		• contractor	
	2. By principal designer if there is a written agreement.	7(1)(c)		• principal contractor	
	For projects with more than one contractor:			• principal designer	
	1. Client duties to be undertaken by principal contractor, or	7(1)(b)			
	2. By principal designer if there is a written agreement.	7(1)(c)			
	NOTE:				
	1. Failure to make principal contractor and/or principal designer appointments ensures that:	7(2)(a)			
	• designer in control of pre-construction phase is the principal designer, and	7(2)(b)			
	• contractor in control of construction phase is the principal contractor.				
	NOTE: NO FURTHER DUTIES are placed on the domestic client, since such duties pass to others by design or default.				

Table A.3 Designer summary CDM 2015

SUMMARY OF DUTIES UNDER THE CDM REGULATIONS 2015

Duty holder	Pre-construction		Construction phase
Designer	**General duties:**		
	1. Must have skills, knowledge and experience as well as organisational capability to fulfil role.	8(1)	
	2. Must not accept appointment unless he fulfils the conditions above.	8(2)	
	3. Must cooperate with others at the same or adjoining site.	8(4)	
	4. Must report any relevant health and safety issue to those in a controlling position.	8(5)	**S T A R T**
	5. Must provide information/instruction as soon as possible in a comprehensible form.	8(6)	**O F**
	6. Must ensure those to be directly appointed have skills, knowledge and experience as well as organisational capability to fulfil role.	8(3)	**C O N S**
	Duties of designers:		**T**
	1. Ensure client is aware of his duties before commencing work.	9(1)	**R U**
	2. Account for general principles of prevention and pre-construction information in any design preparation/modification.	9(2) & 9(3)	**C T**
	3. Provide information about principal risks to principal designer.	9(3)	**I**
	4. Collate appropriate information for inclusion in health and safety file.	9(3)	**O N**
	5. Provide sufficient information to client, other designers and contractors.	9(4)	
	6. Where design is prepared/modified outside Great Britain and commissioned by a designer established in Great Britain, then the appointing designer MUST ensure that Regulation 9 is complied with.	10	
	NOTE:		**E N D O F C O N S T R U C T I O N**
	Domestic client sites with more than one contractor: Failure by client to make appointments ensures the designer in control of the pre-construction phase IS the principal designer.	7(2)(a)	

NOTE:
Designer duties can occur during the construction phase due to:
- procurement strategies; and/or
- temporary works design by contractor(s).

Therefore many of the designer duties will continue into the construction phase.

Table A.4 Principal designer summary CDM 2015

SUMMARY OF DUTIES UNDER THE CDM REGULATIONS 2015

Duty holder	Pre-construction	Construction phase
Principal designer **NOTE:** Every principal designer is also deemed to be a designer.	**General management:** 1. Must have skills, knowledge and experience as well as organisational capability to fulfil role. — 8(1) 2. Must not accept appointment unless conditions above can be met. — 8(2) 3. Must cooperate with others at the same or adjoining site. — 8(4) 4. Must report any relevant health and safety issue to higher management. — 8(5) 5. Must plan, manage and monitor the pre-construction phase and coordinate health and safety matters to ensure project is carried out without risks to health and safety. — 11(1) 6. Must take account of general principles of prevention and the relevant content of the construction phase plan and any health and safety file. — 11(2) 7. Must ensure designers comply with their duties under Reg. 9. — 11(4) 8. Must ensure that all persons working on the pre-construction phase cooperate with the client, principal designer and each other. — 11(5) **Pre-construction information:** 1. Must assist the client in the provision of pre-construction information. — 11(6)(a) 2. Must provide pre-construction information promptly and in a convenient form to every designer and contractor appointed or being considered for appointment. — 11(6)(b) 3. Must prepare a health and safety file appropriate to the characteristics of the project containing information likely to be needed during any subsequent project to ensure the health and safety of any person. — 12(5) **Construction phase plan:** 1. Must assist the principal contractor in the drafting of the construction phase plan by the provision of relevant information. — 12(3) **Health and safety file:** 1. Must prepare a health and safety file. — 12(5) 2. Must identify any point for hand over of file to principal contractor. — 12(8)	**General management:** 1. Must cooperate with others at the same or adjoining site. — 8(4) 2. Must report any relevant health and safety issue to higher management. — 8(5) 3. Must take account of general principles of prevention and the relevant content of the construction phase plan and any health and safety file. — 11(2) 4. Must ensure designers comply with their duties under Reg. 9. — 11(4) **Pre-construction information:** 1. Must assist the client in the provision of pre-construction information. — 11(6)(a) 2. Provide pre-construction information promptly and in a convenient form to every designer and contractor appointed or being considered for appointment. — 11(6)(b) **Construction phase plan:** 1. Must liaise with the principal contractor for the duration of the principal designer's appointment and share with the principal contractor relevant information for planning, managing and monitoring of the construction phase and the coordination of health and safety matters. — 11(7) **Health and safety file:** 1. Must review, update and revise the health and safety file from time to time to take account of any work changes. — 12(6) 2. If the principal designer's appointment concludes before the end of the project, the health and safety file must be passed to the principal contractor. — 12(8) 3. Otherwise, at the end of the project pass the health and safety file to the client. — 12(10)

NOTE: (Domestic client project with more than one contractor)

[1] Client duties could be carried out by the principal designer where there is a written agreement that the principal designer will fulfil those duties. Reg. 7(1)(c).

[2] Failure by client to make appointments ensures the designer in control of the pre-construction phase plan IS the principal designer. Reg. 7(2).

Table A.5 Contractor summary CDM 2015

SUMMARY OF DUTIES UNDER THE CDM REGULATIONS 2015

Duty holder	Pre-construction		Construction phase	
Contractor	**General management:** 1. Must have skills, knowledge and experience as well as organisational capability to fulfil role.	8(1)	**General management:** 1. Ensure all appointees have the skills, knowledge experience and operational capabilities to satisfactorily fulfil their role.	8(1) & 8(3)
	2. Must not accept appointment unless they fulfil the conditions above.	8(2)	2. Must not accept appointment unless the conditions above can be fulfilled.	8(2)
	Note: Only one contractor (domestic client site): Client duties as per Regulations 4(1) to (7) and 6 MUST be undertaken by the contractor.	7(1)(a)	3. Must cooperate with others at the same or adjoining site.	8(4)
			4. Must report any relevant health and safety issue to those in control.	8(5)
			5. Must provide relevant information/instruction promptly in a comprehensible form.	8(6)
			6. Must not carry out construction work unless satisfied that client is aware of the client's duties.	15(1)
			7. Must plan, manage and monitor construction work under his control so that it is carried out safely.	15(2)
	More than one contractor (domestic client site): Failure by client to make appointments ensures the contractor in control of the construction phase plan IS the principal contractor.	7(2)(b)	8. Must not employ/appoint a person to work on a construction site unless he has or is in the process of obtaining the necessary, skill, knowledge, training and experience etc.	15(7)
			9. Must provide appropriate supervision, instruction and training to each worker. Must provide a suitable site induction, information on critical procedures to be followed and risk relevant information.	15(8) 15(9)
	Note: Contractors can also incur designer duties in respect of temporary works design. Part 4 (Regulations 16 to 35) imposes 'General requirements for all construction sites' on all those who manage site construction work.		10. Must ensure reasonable steps have been taken to prevent access by unauthorised persons.	15(10)
			11. Must ensure welfare facilities are appropriate.	15(11)
			Only one contractor: 1. Where more than one contractor, must comply with directions of principal contractor and/or principal designer and relevant methodology in construction phase plan.	15(3)
			2. Must account for general principles of prevention.	15(4)
			3. Must draft a construction phase plan or make arrangements for it to be drawn up.	15(4)

Table A.6 Principal contractor summary CDM 2015

SUMMARY OF DUTIES UNDER THE CDM REGULATIONS 2015

Duty holder	Pre-construction		Construction phase	
Principal contractor **NOTE:** **Every principal contractor is also deemed to be a contractor**	**General management:** 1. Must have skills, knowledge and experience as well as organisational capability to fulfil role.	8(1)	**General management:** 1. As per the duties on other dutyholders, e.g. contractor(s), outlined in Regs 8(1), 8(2), 8(3), 8(4), 8(5) and 8(6). As per items 1 to 5 under 'General management' for 'Contractor'.	13(1)
	2. Must not accept appointment unless the conditions above can be fulfilled.	8(2)	2. Must plan, manage and monitor the construction phase and coordinate health and safety matters to ensure construction work is carried out without risks to health and safety.	13(2)
	3. Must cooperate with others at the same or adjoining site.	8(4)	3. Must take account of the general principles of prevention.	13(3)(a)
	4. Must report any relevant health and safety issue to those above.	8(5)	4. Must organise cooperation between contractors; coordinate implementation by contractors of applicable legal requirements for health and safety; ensure employers and self-employed apply general principles of prevention and follow relevant provisions of the construction phase plan.	13(3)(a) to 13(3)(c)
	5. Necessary information/instruction must be comprehensible and provided asap.	8(6)	5. Must ensure: • site induction provided • prohibition of entry to the unauthorised • welfare facilities are provided.	13(4)
	Construction phase plan: 1. Must draft a construction phase plan or make arrangements for it to be drawn up.	12(1)	6. Must liaise with principal designer during his appointment and share with the principal designer information relevant to the planning, management and monitoring of the pre-construction phase and the coordination of health and safety matters during the pre-construction phase.	13(5)
	NOTE: Domestic client More than one contractor: Client duties as per Regs 4(1) to (7) and 6 MUST be undertaken by the principal contractor. Failure by client to make appointments ensures the contractor in control of the construction phase plan IS the principal contractor if it is foreseeable that more than one contractor will be on site at any one time.	12(1)	**Construction phase plan:** 1. Must ensure that the construction phase plan is appropriately reviewed, updated and revised from time to time compatible with the programme of works.	12(4)
	PART 4 (Regulations 16 to 35) imposes **'General requirements for all construction sites' on all those who manage site construction work.**		**Consultation and engagement with workers:** 1. Must make and maintain arrangements for effective cooperation between principal contractor and workers to develop, promote and check health and safety control measures.	14(1)(a)
			2. Must consult workers or their representatives in good time on health and safety matters.	14(1)(b)
			3. Must ensure workers or their representatives can inspect and take copies of health and safety-related information provided to the principal contractor.	14(1)(c)
			Health and safety file: 1. Must provide the principal designer with any information in his possession relevant to the health and safety file.	12(7)
			2. If the health and safety file is passed to the principal contractor by the principal designer (in case of early termination of appointment as per procurement strategy), then the principal contractor must ensure that it is reviewed, updated and revised from time to time to account for work changes etc. and handed over to the client at the end of the project.	12(9)
			3. If there is no principal designer then the principal contractor must pass the health and safety file to the client at the end of the project.	12(10)

(Vertical column markers between the Pre-construction and Construction phase columns read: "START OF CONSTRUCTION" and "END OF CONSTRUCTION".)

A.2 Effective Management Arrangements

Factors related to the EFFECTIVENESS OF MANAGEMENT ARRANGEMENTS (Reg[ns] 4(1) and 4(3))

Dutyholder	Heading	Description	Reg[n]	Yes	No
		NOTE: The following are meant to provide client guidance on factors which could constitute evidence of the establishment and ongoing effectiveness of management arrangements.			
	General	Have all appointees been assessed for skills, knowledge and experience together with organisational capability (only applicable to organisations) to fulfil the role?	8(1)		
		Similarly with all those appointed by other dutyholders?	8(3)		
		Have all parties with whom cooperation is required been identified?	8(4)		
		Are all such parties duly cooperating?	8(4)		
		Is all relevant information/instruction provided by the dutyholders comprehensible and being provided promptly?	8(6)		
		Is the principal designer's role terminating before the end of the project?	12(8)		
Designer	Design process	Is there demonstrable evidence of the discharge of the general principles of prevention?	9(2)		
		Is information on residual hazards being passed to the principal designer?	9(3)		
		Is relevant information being provided to the client, other designers and contractors?	9(4)		
		Is any design being undertaken outside Great Britain?	10		
		Is the commissioning party based in Great Britain?	10(1)(a)		
		Are there any implications for the client?	10(1)(b)		
	PC Information	Have reasonable attempts been made to provide relevant information?	4(4)		
		Is appropriate residual hazard information being provided to the principal designer?	9(3)		
	CP Plan	Is appropriate residual hazard information being provided to designers and contractors?	9(4)		
	Health and safety file	Is appropriate residual hazard information being provided to the principal designer?	9(3)(a)		
	Information	Is appropriate residual hazard information being provided to the principal designer?	9(4)		

NOTE: In the communication of information, the client should be aware that consideration must be given to single contractor and multiple-contractor sites, both of which need to receive pre-construction information and deliver a construction phase plan.

Principal designer	**Design management process**	Is there demonstrable evidence of the discharge of the general principles of prevention?	9(2)		
		Is information on residual hazards being passed to the principal designer?	9(3)		
		Is relevant information being provided to the client, other designers and contractors?	9(4)		
		Is any design being undertaken outside Great Britain?	10(1)		
		Is the commissioning party based in Great Britain?	10(1)(b		
		Are there any Regulation 9 implications for the client?			
		Is the principal designer accounting for:			
		• the general principles of prevention?	11(2)		
		• the content of any construction phase plan?	11(2)		
		• the content of any health and safety file?	11(2)		
		Are all designers complying with their Regulation 9 duties?	11(4)		
	PC Information	Has the coordination of information for the pre-construction phase identified all contributors?	11(5)		
		Is there suitable cooperation between all contributors and the client, principal designer and each other?	11(5)		
		Is PC Information being promptly provided to all designers and appointed contractors and those under consideration?	11(6)		
	Construction phase	Is there satisfactory liaison with the principal contractor in respect of health and safety matters?	11(7) 12(3)		
	Health and safety file	Has the management of the health and safety file begun?	12(5)		
		Is this management process being reviewed, updated and revised at frequent intervals during the construction phase?	12(6)		
		Has a handover time been agreed with the principal contractor for his management of this document (if relevant)?	12(8)		
		Has a date been agreed for the handover of this document to the client/principal contractor?	12(10)		

(Continued)

Factors related to the EFFECTIVENESS OF MANAGEMENT ARRANGEMENTS (Reg^{ms} 4(1) and 4(3))

Dutyholder	Heading	Description	Regⁿ	Yes	No
		NOTE: Many of the above items are part of the project dynamics and have to be revisited and affirmed at regular intervals throughout the design and construction stages.			
Contractor	CP Plan	**ONLY APPLICABLE TO THE SINGLE CONTRACTOR SITE (otherwise a duty of the principal contractor)**			
		Is this document:			
		• sufficiently developed for the start of the construction phase?	15(5)		
		• compatible with the current programme of works?	15(6)		
		• compatible with the latest design changes?	15(6)		
	General management	Is cooperation effective with other persons and those on adjoining sites?	8(4)		
		Are health and safety management arrangements effective on this site?	15(2)		
		Have any improvement/prohibition notices been issued?	15(2)		
		Is there compliance with directions given by:			
		• principal contractor?	15(3)(a)		
		• principal designer?*	15(3)(a)		
		• relevant parts of the construction phase plan?	15(3)(b)		
		Are all operatives competent or under the supervision of a competent person?	15(7)		
		Has each worker been provided with appropriate supervision/instruction and information for work to be undertaken without risks to health and safety?	15(8)		
	Site security	Is the site secure?	15(10)		
		Have all damaged areas been repaired?	15(10)		
		Have there been any breaches since the last progress meeting?	15(10)		
	Welfare	Are welfare facilities compatible with the requirements of Schedule 2?	15(11)		
		Any issues arising from the current welfare service report?	15(11)		
	Health and safety file	Is relevant information being passed to the principal contractor?	8(6)		
		NOTE:* This requires the contractor (on a multiple-contractor site) to comply with directions of the principal designer. Standard protocol and practice to date channels all such access via the principal contractor, which remains the preferred option.	15(3)(a)		

Principal contractor	Pre-construction phase	Is liaison ongoing with the principal designer throughout the appointment period for the purpose of sharing relevant information for the management of health and safety during the pre-construction phase?	13(5)		
	CP Plan	Is this document: • sufficiently developed to allow the start of the construction phase? • compatible with the current programme of works? • compatible with the latest design changes? Has the client provided all relevant information?	12(1) 12(4) 12(4) 4(4)		
	General management	Are health and safety management arrangements effective on this site? Has account been taken of the general principles of prevention? Have all contractors been identified? Has a cooperating mechanism been established and cooperating parties identified? Are all employers and the self-employed operating towards the general principles of prevention?	13(1) 13(2) 13(3) 13(3) 13(3)		
	Site induction	Has a site induction been provide to all operatives? Have all inductees been entered onto the site induction register?	13(4) 13(4)		
	Site security	Is the site secure? Have all damaged areas been repaired? Have there been any breaches since the last progress meeting?	13(4)(c) 13(4)(c) 13(4)(b)		
	Welfare	Are all welfare facilities compliant with Schedule 2? Have all welfare service report items been effectively undertaken?	13(4)(b) 13(4)(b)		
	Health and safety file	Has relevant information for the health and safety file been passed to the principal designer?	12(7)		
Principal contractor/ continued					

(Continued)

Factors related to the EFFECTIVENESS OF MANAGEMENT ARRANGEMENTS (Reg^{ns} 4(1) and 4(3))

Dutyholder	Heading	Description	Reg^m	Yes	No
		Will the management of this document pass to the principal contractor at any stage?	12(8)		
		If so has the principal contractor determined the acceptability and currency of its contents ?	12(9)		
		If acceptable is the principal contractor reviewing, updating and revising this document at frequent intervals during the construction phase?			
		Has a date been agreed for the handover of this document?	12(10)		
	Consultation and engagement	Are arrangements for the enablement of effective cooperation with workers on health and safety matters:	14(a)		
		• established?	14(a)		
		• remaining effective?	14(b)		
		Are workers/representatives being consulted in good time on health and safety matters?	14(c)		
		Have arrangements been made to allow workers/representatives access to relevant information?			

NOTE:

1. Any number of the above points would often be addressed in the normal agenda items of both the design review/site progress meetings. Where there are gaps in the corresponding items covered, the client and his professional advisors should look to finetune and capture the affirmation or otherwise in an agenda restructuring or temporarily under Any Other Business.

2. It would be a reflection on the lack of supporting culture if too many of these items, at appropriate times, had to be dealt with as additions to the normal business of any meeting.

3. The client duty regarding the establishment and effectiveness of management arrangements thereafter should not be pursued with unnecessary bureaucratic vigour. Existing procedures such as pre-start meetings and meeting agendas provide the vehicle by which affirmation of the chosen selection of salient points could be achieved, and such affirmation evidenced by the corresponding minutes.

(Reg items for NOTE row: 4(1), 4(3))

Bibliography

Carpenter, JZ (2006) *Competency and Resource*, HSE RR422, HSE Books.

CDM 2007 Construction work sector guidance for designers (C662), O Arup and Partners, CIRIA, London, 2007.

Construction (Design and Management) Regulations 2007. Approved Code of Practice, Managing Health and Safety in Construction (L144), HSE Books, 2007.

Construction (Design and Management) Regulations 2007, HMSO Statutory Instrument 2007 No. 320, The Stationery Office Limited, London, 2007.

Five Steps to Risk Assessment, INDG 163 (rev. 1), HSE Books, 1998.

Management of Health and Safety at Work Regulations 1999. Approved Code of Practice and Guidance (L121), 2nd edn, HSE Books, 2000.

Newsletters (published approximately every two months), The Association for Project Safety, 12 Stanhope Place, Edinburgh EH12 5HH.

Practice Notes (published approximately every two months), The Association for Project Safety, 12 Stanhope Place, Edinburgh EH12 5HH.

Research Report 218, Peer Review of Analysis of Specialist Group Reports on Causes of Construction Accidents, HSE Books, 2004.

Research Report 422, Developing Guidelines for the Selection of Designers and Contractors under the Construction (Design and Management) Regulations 1994, HSE Books, 2005.

Rethinking Construction: The Report of the Construction Taskforce, chaired by Sir John Egan, Department of the Environment, Transport and the Regions, London, 1998.

Revitalising Health and Safety in Construction, Discussion Document, HSE Books, 2002.

Successful Health and Safety Management, HSG 65, 2nd edn, HSE Books, 1997.

Summerhayes, SD (2002) *CDM Procedures Manual*, 2nd edn, Blackwell Publishing, Oxford.

Workplace Health, Safety and Welfare. Workplace (Health, Safety and Welfare) Regulations 1992. Approved Code of Practice (L24), HSE Books, 1992.

CDM Regulations 2015 Procedures Manual, Fourth Edition. Stuart D. Summerhayes.
© 2016 John Wiley & Sons, Ltd. Published 2016 by John Wiley & Sons, Ltd.

Web directory

No.	Page	Description
1	www.aps.org.uk	The Association for Project Safety
2	www.bre.co.uk	Building Research Establishment
3	www.cibse.org	Chartered Institute of Building Services Engineers
4	www.thecc.org.uk	Construction Confederation
5	www.constructingexcellence.org.uk	Constructing Excellence
6	www.cic.org.uk	Construction Industry Council
7	www.citb.org.uk	Construction Industry Training Board
8	www.cpa.uk	Construction Plant Hire Association
9	www.dti.org.uk	Department of Trade and Industry
10	www.agency.osha.eu.int	European Agency for Safety and Health at Work
11	www.hse.gov.uk	Health and Safety Executive: United Kingdom
12	www.hsebooks.com	Health and Safety Executive Books
13	www.hsa.ie	Health and Safety Authority: Ireland
14	www.ice.org.uk	The Institution of Civil Engineers
15	www.imeche.org.uk	The Institution of Mechanical Engineers
16	www.istructe.org.uk	The Institution of Structural Engineers
17	www.nao.org.uk	National Audit Office
18	www.demolition-nfdc.com	National Federation of Demolition Contractors
19	www.nhbc.co.uk	National House-Building Council
20	www.ogc.gov.uk	Office of Government Commerce
21	www.eustatistics.gov.uk	Office for National Statistics
22	www.pff.org.uk	Precast Flooring Federation
23	www.rias.org.uk	The Royal Incorporation of Architects in Scotland
24	www.architecture.com	Royal Institute of British Architects
25	www.rics.org	The Royal Institution of Chartered Surveyors
26	www.rospa.com	The Royal Society for the Prevention of Accidents
27	www.safetyindesign.org	Safety in Design Ltd
28	www.scoss.org.uk	Standing Committee on Structural Safety
29	www.strategicforum.org.uk	Strategic Forum

Web directory

CDM Regulations 2015 Procedures Manual, Fourth Edition. Stuart D. Summerhayes.
© 2016 John Wiley & Sons, Ltd. Published 2016 by John Wiley & Sons, Ltd.

Index

CDM Regulations 2015 Procedures Manual, Fourth Edition. Stuart D. Summerhayes.
© 2016 John Wiley & Sons, Ltd. Published 2016 by John Wiley & Sons, Ltd.